Y0-BRT-967

The
INTERNATIONAL HEBREW HERITAGE LIBRARY

The
INTERNATIONAL
HEBREW

INTERNATIONAL BOOK CORPORATION
MIAMI, FLORIDA

HERITAGE

LIBRARY

By the Editors of
The Israeli Publishing Institute, Jerusalem, B. M.

VOLUME IV:

JEWISH NOBEL PRIZE WINNERS

EDITORIAL STAFF
for the International Hebrew Heritage Library

Table of Contents

FOREWORD

Perhaps the greatest honor the world can confer on an individual, in recognition of significant contributions to the fields of science, literature, and the art of peace, is the well-known Nobel Prize.

Recently, an Israeli writer, S. Y. Agnon, was awarded the Nobel Prize in literature. In the past, other Jewish recipients of this international mark of recognition were Niels Bohr, famous for his pioneering research in atomic science; Albert Einstein, for his theory of relativity in the field of physics; Paul Ehrlich, for his brilliant research in immunology; and Boris Pasternak, the author of *Dr. Zhivago,* for his contribution to modern literature.

Many Jews, in addition to those mentioned above, have been winners of the Nobel Prize. Indeed, Jews form by far the largest single ethnic or national group of Nobel Laureates, a quite astounding statistic when one recalls what a small minority they are in the world at large.

The variety of contributions to scientific progress, literary creativity, and the furtherance of peace, reflected in the works of numerous Nobel award winners of Jewish origin, can only reflect on the far flung scope of their concern for and interest in the problems and needs of their fellow men.

That many of them distinguished themselves in many spheres of human endeavor is a tribute to their capacity to understand the need for a continuous, ever-widening and expanding interest in the manifold developments in scientific research, literary expression, and the promotion of peace, so that humanity may realize its positive capacity for the control of its physical environment, within the framework of social progress towards peace and the eventual realization of international disarmament.

Israel Renov, D.H.L., Ph.D.
Professor, City University of New York

ACKNOWLEDGEMENTS

The Editors wish to express their thanks to the various agencies and organizations whose invaluable assistance made this work possible. These include: The Zionist Archives, Jerusalem and New York; The Jewish National Fund, Jerusalem and New York; Keren Hayesod, Jerusalem; Beth Jabotinsky, Tel Aviv; YIVO Institute, New York; Union of American Hebrew Congregations, New York; New York Public Library; Hadassah, New York; The Nobel Foundation, Stockholm; The Leo Baeck Institute, New York; The National Foundation, New York; The New York Philharmonic Society; the Esperanto League for North America, New York; American Jewish Archives, Cincinnati; Jewish Theological Seminary, New York; and others. A detailed list of picture credits appears at the end of the Index.

Also gratefully acknowledged are the efforts and labors of Jeanne Kuebler, Eli Flatto, Barbara Northrop, and Joanna Smart for their editorial assistance; Amos Kasimirsky for work on production and layout; Charles Cassidy for special artwork; and Tove and Ira Solomon for additional research and photographs.

VOLUME IV:

JEWISH NOBEL PRIZE WINNERS

SHMUEL YOSEF AGNON
1888-

Agnon is generally recognized as the foremost living author of Hebrew literature. In 1966 he was awarded the Nobel Prize for literature for his "profoundly characteristic narrative art, with motifs from the life of the Jewish people." Edmund Wilson saw in him a "true representative of that great line of Jewish writers that begins with the authors of Genesis." Arnold Band, associate professor of Hebrew at the University of California, who wrote a book on Agnon, *Nostalgia and Nightmare in the Fiction of S.Y. Agnon*, characterized as the prime force motivating Agnon's best works — the honest confrontation with reality.

Agnon's career began in 1907, when the author S. Ben Zion published in the newspaper *Ha-Omer* an early story of his under his given name Tchatchkes, son of Rabbi Shalom Mordecai Halevy, the rabbi of Butchach in East Galicia. The title of the story was "Agunot" (Deserted Women), and he adopted his pen name from the title of this first successful effort. Since that time his tales of Jewish life in the Diaspora and in Palestine have gained him a unique place in Hebrew literature. His early life was spent in Galicia, and although he settled in Palestine in 1909, he lived in Germany from 1912-1923. Fittingly, he was the first Jewish recipient of the Nobel Prize who won this coveted honor as an Israeli, not as a German, American, or Frenchman.

Agnon is regarded as the great epic writer of modern Hebrew literature, and his works have a symbolic content mingling reality and imagination. Although he is first and foremost a storyteller, his tales do not rely on rich imaginative plots or surprising action, but instead focus on the inner lives of his characters.

The sensitive reader of Agnon's works cannot escape the persistent irony of tone. The almost deliberately futile preoccupation with nostalgia, usually handled as fantasy, is juxtaposed against a consciousness that the world he yearns for is no more. Unlike many other writers in Hebrew and Yiddish, Agnon has never been satisfied with the banal romanticizing of Eastern European Jewry or even of Galicia itself, where he was born. If he has lavished loving

With the presentation of a bouquet of flowers, the Swedish consul in Jerusalem notifies Agnon that he has been awarded the Nobel Prize

attention upon the Hasidim of Galicia and Podolia, he has done so to spin a literary myth around his own experience and imagination.

In his uncompromising artistic integrity (a difficult stance to maintain during two generations of intense ideological ferment), in his persistent preoccupation with the central spiritual concerns of this century, and in his dedication to esthetic perfection, Agnon also moves in the mainstream of sophisticated European and American literature.

Among his many works are *The Bridal Canopy,* depicting Jewish Galicia in the early 19th century and, like most of his work, rich in folklore; *A Wayfarer Tarries the Night,* which describes the inner ruin of the Jewish village in Galicia in the period between the two World Wars; and *The Book of Tales,* stories of fantasy and horror.

ROBERT BARANY
1876-1936

A gift for knowing when not to take things for granted led Dr. Robert Barany, an Austrian physician, to an important medical discovery. As an ear specialist, he often had to wash out patients' ears, and many complained that this made them dizzy. Barany also noticed a strange circular movement of the eye would occur at the same time the ear was being washed. He decided to investigate the relationship between ear-washing, dizziness and eye movement.

One day a patient noticed that when the nurse used warm water for the washing, there was no dizziness; only cold water produced this effect. Dr. Barany directed the nurse to wash the next patient's ears with *hot* water. Dizziness was still present, but this time the eyes rolled in the *opposite* direction.

Because similar disturbances occur when the ear is infected, Barany wanted to find out why temperature change in a healthy ear causes dizziness and eye movements. He knew that the cochlea and semicircular canals in the inner ear are full of fluids. He reasoned that the application of heat or cold causes circulation of the fluid in the ear, just as heated or chilled water circulates — with the hot water rising, and the cold water sinking.

Since the nerves of eye and ear are related, movement of the ear fluids causes corresponding movement of the eyes. Barany discovered that by washing the external ear, he could ascertain the health of the inner ear. The eye will not move if the ear is ailing. This diagnostic test came to be used by doctors everywhere, and it helped to cut the death rate from internal ear infections from a high of 50 per cent to almost no deaths at all.

Barany continued to work on dizziness, ear-noises, the maintenance of equilibrium and temperature changes. He investigated the cerebellum — the coordinating brain center for muscular movement — and its reaction to temperature changes in the ear.

He found that malfunction in the cerebellum can be diagnosed by noting eye movement, and that when the temperature in the ear is changed, equilibrium is affected.

During World War I, Barany had the opportunity to prove his

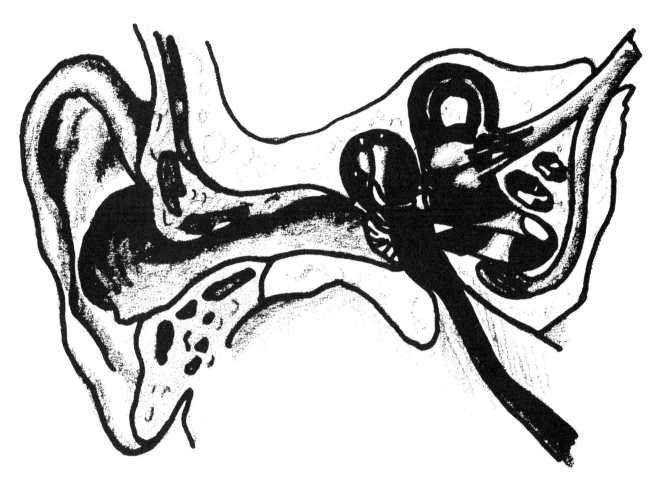

Diagram of the middle ear

theory. As a doctor in the Austrian Army, he treated many cases of head wounds where skulls had been cut open. Instead of cooling the ear to cause eye movement, Barany cooled parts of the cerebellum which could now be reached. His theory that brain injury could also be diagnosed by eye movement proved accurate.

During the war, he also developed techniques of limiting infections and treating them. After his capture by the Russians, he was put in charge of a hospital by his captors until a prisoner-of-war exchange, when he was allowed to return to Austria. In 1917 he went to Uppsala, Sweden, where he became professor at the University and the head of a hospital.

As a result of the horror and destruction he saw in the war, Barany became a pacifist and spent the rest of his life working for peace as well as for medicine.

Dr. Barany received the 1914 Nobel Prize in Medicine for his contributions to the curse of diseases of the ear, the brain and the nervous system.

HENRI BERGSON
1859-1941

Most philosophers deal with matters so lofty and so esoteric that they are understood only by other philosophers and scholars. Henri Bergson, however, was that rare philosopher who wrote with such clarity on questions close to the hearts of all men that he touched the minds of the common people. His lectures were filled to overflowing, and his books — notably *Laughter* and *Creative Evolution* — have been widely read.

Bergson's works represent a reaction against the mechanistic theories of his day, which saw man and the universe as a complicated machine, predictable and manipulatable. He viewed the world as a continuing process of creative evolution, hence of inevitable novelty and change, rather than the result of fixed natural laws. His almost mystical view of intuition as the source of real knowledge influenced such important creative minds as Marcel Proust.

Pondering the very basis and purpose of existence, Bergson sought explanations of the creative process beyond the evolutionary theories held by the thinkers of his day. It was not enough that life evolved through a process of "natural selection," whereby only creatures capable of adaptation to their environment survived and flourished. There must be something else, Bergson reasoned; a creative force common to all organisms which enables them to carry on the struggle for survival. He named this vital life force the *élan vital*.

Bergson contends that the *élan vital* exists in every cell of every living organism and is the perpetual energy which first created life billions of years ago. It is this same force which is responsible for the countless varieties of life that arose in the world.

In another vein, Bergson imagined the independent but interrelated functions of the intangible mind, the emotions and the brain. The brain, he said, is capable of incredibly complex calculations and analyses. It is the mind, however, which holds the intuitive force, through which comes all knowledge of reality. Lastly, Bergson theorized, it is the emotions that give life its nobility, beauty and meaning.

Bergson at study

In his essays on time, Bergson drew a distinction between "time" as an artificially created concept of seconds, minutes and hours, as opposed to real time, which he called "duration." He described "duration" as "the continuing progress of the past which gnaws into the future and which swells as it advances." Moreover, Bergson believed that each moment of living is a kind of creation which cannot be precisely predicted.

Born in Paris of Jewish-Polish-English parents, Bergson did not become a French citizen until he was 21 years old. A mathematical genius, at the age of 18 he solved a complex mathematical problem and his solution was published in a scientific journal. But Bergson's overwhelming life interest was in the study and teaching of philosophy. He was for many years a professor at the Collège de France. In 1914 he was elected to the French Academy and in 1927 was awarded the Nobel Prize for Literature.

Although he never actively practiced Judaism, Bergson avidly protested the anti-Semitic legislation of the Vichy government after the fall of France in 1940. When France's puppet government set up an office for the required registration of all Jews, Bergson, because of his renown, was offered exemption by the officials. He refused the privilege and later soberly explained, "I wanted to remain among those who tomorrow will be persecuted." Ill and in his 80's, he took his place in line at the registration office. A few months later he was dead.

FELIX BLOCH
1905-

When a scientist has one of his discoveries named after him, it is a great honor. Professor Felix Bloch, who has been involved in all of the important stages of the development of nuclear energy, has been accorded this tribute five times: the literature of atomic research makes frequent reference to "Bloch's Wall," "Bloch's Law," "Bloch's Reactions," "Bloch-Floquet Principle" and "Bloch-Gruneisen Ratios."

After graduating from the Technical College in Zurich, his native town, Bloch headed for Leipzig, Germany, then the center of atomic research. The young Swiss Jew became first the pupil, then the assistant to one of the outstanding scientists of the time, Werner Heisenberg, who is known as "the father of quantum mechanics." Bloch was appointed lecturer in theoretical physics at Leipzig University, where he had received his doctorate only four years before.

Still in his 20's, Bloch astounded the scientific world with his discoveries of the principles regulating chain reactions of electrons within a crystal (the "Bloch-Floquet Principle"). The second law, "Bloch-Gruneisen Ratios," describes the electrical properties of metals in various temperatures. "Bloch's Wall" describes a transition stage between two parts of a magnetic crystal which the magnet influences in different directions. His reputation was enhanced by his books, originally published in the German language. Because of their importance, they were immediately translated into English and French. In these books, Bloch posed several theories concerning the properties of electrons of metals, and also dealt with static and magnetic problems.

After Hitler's rise to power, Bloch fled Germany and lectured at the Henri Poincaré Institute in Paris. Later he cooperated with the eminent scientist Enrico Fermi in Rome. The fame of the young scientist preceded him, and he was invited to become a professor at one of the largest centers of atomic research in Stanford, California.

Bloch first met Albert Einstein in 1939, at Princeton University, and from this time on, the two physicists kept in regular contact. Soon after Einstein's famous letter to President Franklin Delano Roosevelt, pointing out the importance of the United States having atomic power before Germany, the center for the manufacture of the atom bomb was established. Bloch agreed to

Dr. Felix Bloch at work in his laboratory

work on this historic project in Los Alamos with Professor Robert Oppenheimer.

With the completion of his work in Los Alamos, Bloch studied radar techniques in the radio laboratory of Harvard University. As a result, he developed the original idea that it is possible to track movements of particles of the atom nucleus by means of techniques usually used in receiving radio waves. It was Bloch who first suggested that the signals which would be apparent would

Dr. Bloch in his Stamford laboratory with a nuclear induction spectometer, used in determining properties of atomic nuclei

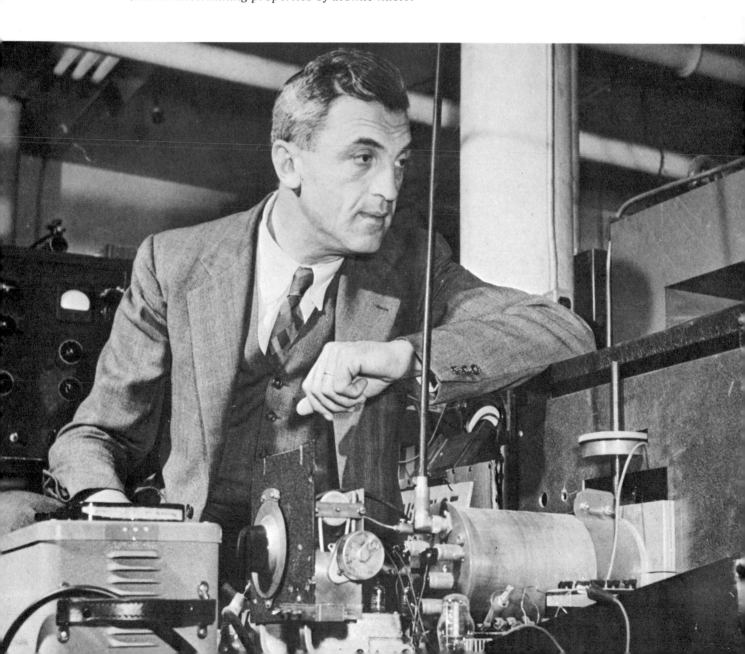

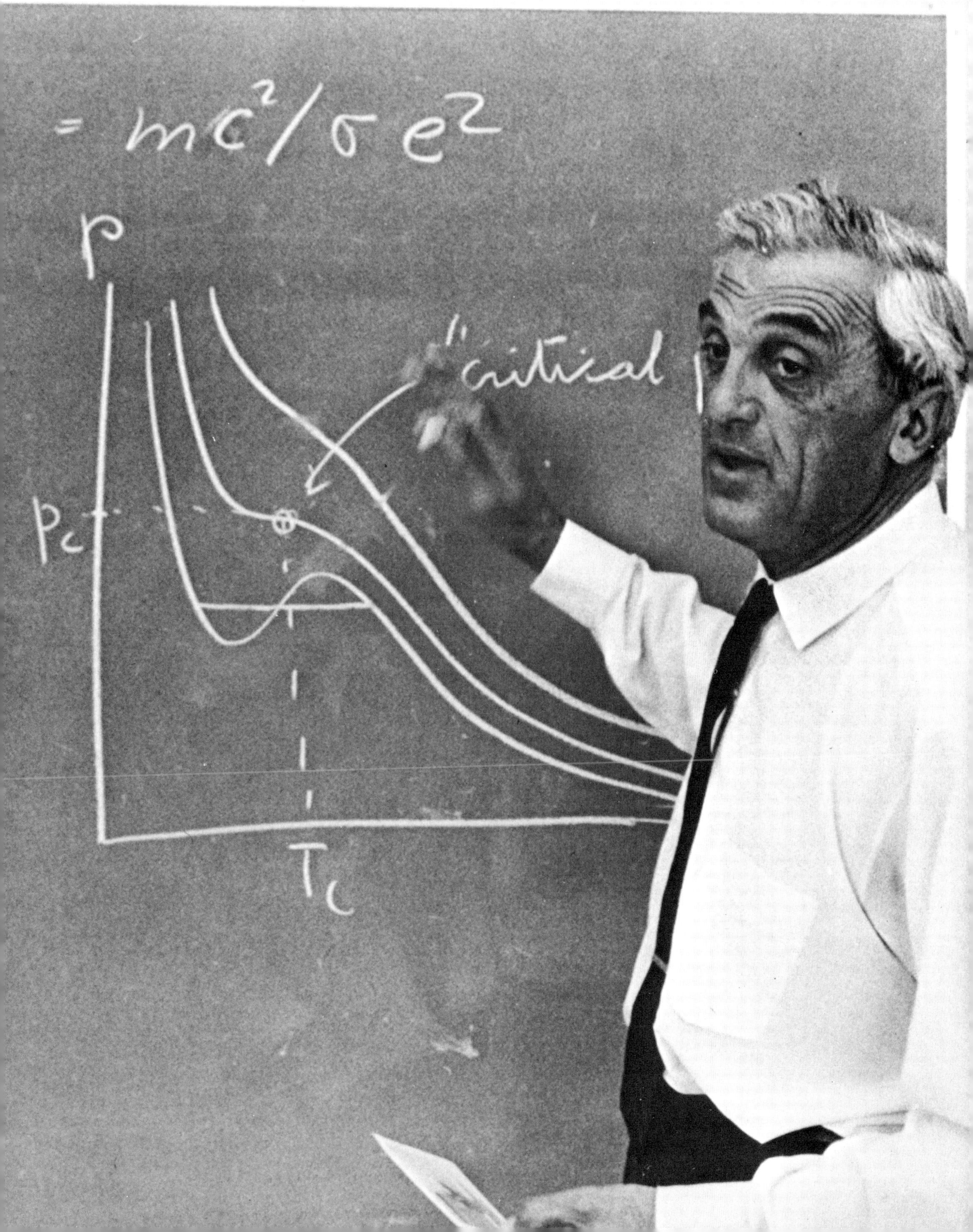
= mc²/σ e²
p
"critical
pc
Tc

originate in electromagnetic induction. His system is therefore known as "nuclear induction." It describes with relative simplicity and considerable accuracy the direction of the lines on the radar screen which indicate whether the nucleii are turning in the direction of the field or in a counter-direction.

In 1952, Bloch received the Nobel Prize for his work on nuclear magnetism. Two years later, he was elected by the delegates from 12 nations to direct the European Nuclear Center in Geneva. The purpose of this center was to produce radioactive isotopes for peaceful purposes, recognizing that atomic energy should be used to benefit mankind instead of to destroy it.

NIELS BOHR
1885-1962

It is September 1943, and the Nazi occupation authorities have just taken over the government in Denmark. The few Jews remaining in the country know that they will be hunted down, and therefore look for a hiding place or a means of escape. On a dark night, a group of people huddle together, shivering, by the sea. After a long wait, a small rowboat glides soundlessly to the shore, and the people tumble in as the boat pulls out on its way to Sweden and safety. Among them is Niels Bohr, the great atomic physicist.

Bohr was the son of a Jewish mother and Danish father. His father was a professor at the University of Copenhagen, where Niels later studied and taught. There were other famous scientists in the family. Niels began to study physics in 1903, and in 1907, when only twenty-two years old, he published his first research paper, which earned him praise from European scientists and a gold medal from the Danish Academy of Science.

Bohr completed his studies in 1911, and went to England a year later to work with Professor Ernest Rutherford. This was a great opportunity for the young physicist, as Rutherford was one of the leading figures in the world of science. Niels Bohr rose rapidly in the field of atomic physics, working on some of the most important research of the time. In 1920, he was elected to the Danish Academy of Science, and in 1921 became director of the Institute of Theoretical Physics in Copenhagen, which he had helped to found, and which was to become the leading institute in the field of atomic research. A year later, Bohr was awarded the Nobel Prize for Physics for his research on the structure of the atom.

Bohr played a decisive role in the dramatic race between the United States and Germany to build the first atom bomb. In 1939, he was invited to the famous Institute for Advanced Study in Princeton, to work with Professor Albert Einstein. When Bohr arrived in the United States on January 16, 1939, an important telegram from his fellow-researchers in Denmark was waiting for him. Continuing the work that Bohr had started, they had proved that it really was possible to split the uranium atom. Bohr had been the

Professor Bohr (left) chats with the late U.N. Secretary General Dag Hammarskjold, as they await the opening of ceremonies at which they received honorary degrees from Columbia University in 1954

first to discover how to isolate this material — a step which was the precondition for releasing atomic energy. Before long, Bohr's research turned into a top-secret military project: an entire city of 75,000 scientists and technicians was assembled in the desert at Oak Ridge, and all its inhabitants were involved in working in absolute secrecy on one project — the development of the atom bomb.

In the meantime, Niels Bohr returned to Copenhagen to "keep an eye" on Germany's efforts to beat the Americans in the atomic race. In 1942, an officer in the Danish Embassy in Berlin received top military information about a secret weapon that the Nazis were testing, a mysterious bomb which was capable of destroying everything within a radius of 300 yards from where it fell. He also found out that, due to a serious accident in a German laboratory, everyone in the building had been found dead without any visible injuries. Although the entire affair was kept secret by the Germans, it was rumored that the people had been killed by the air pressure built up in the process of creating the atom bomb. In addition to this information, the Danish officer managed to obtain a secret report sent by the German scientists to their Minister of War, in which 72 experimental atomic explosions were described in detail. He passed this report on to the Danish Minister of War, who then rushed it to Professor Niels Bohr. On the basis of the report, Bohr advised the Allies that, although the Germans were doing everything feasible to develop the atomic weapon, they had not yet succeeded in doing so.

Aware of Bohr's tremendous knowledge in the atomic field, Gestapo agents tried to track him down when he escaped from Denmark to Sweden in 1943. They wanted him to instruct their scientists on how to isolate uranium 235, the most important element in the atom bomb. The Swedish police, learning of this, immediately tried to inform Bohr of the Gestapo's intent, but he was, at that moment, on a train to Stockholm. Finally, policemen in a speeding car managed to overtake his train, stop it, and bring Bohr to a hiding place. After a secret telephone conversation with British

Prime Minister Winston Churchill, Bohr was brought to safety in England, where he supervised the research that was to prove so crucial to the Allies' security.

Although Niels Bohr's research provided the starting point in the assembling of the first atom bomb, he personally did not play a direct part in it. Even though he had spent so much of his life

Dr. Bohr (left) with officials of the Rockefeller Institute which in 1962 presented him with an honorary degree

on atomic weapons research, Bohr, as a lover of mankind, always wanted to see atomic energy used for peace.

MELVIN CALVIN
1911-

Photosynthesis — the process by which plants convert water and carbon dioxide from the atmosphere into carbohydrates — has long been one of nature's most intriguing mysteries. Despite the efforts of many scientific investigators to solve this riddle, we cannot yet fully explain the work of the "sugar factory" which operates in every plant. Some of the puzzle was unravelled by the great German-Jewish chemist, Richard Willstätter (1872-1942), who was the first to analyze chlorophyll, known to be necessary to the process. Willstätter received the Nobel Prize for chemistry in 1915 "for research on coloring matter in the vegetable kingdom, principally chlorophyll." He formulated the *theory of assimilation,* which assumed that the sunlight which is absorbed in the plant does its chemical work within the chlorophyll molecule itself.

An American chemist, Melvin Calvin, continued Willstätter's work, in method as well as object. From 1935 on, Calvin devoted himself to investigating the basic process of the conversion of the sun's light and heat by green plants in order to understand the way in which chlorophyll accomplishes its task. It was already established that carbon dioxide enters the plant and appears in all plant materials. Calvin decided to shorten the "traveling time" in order to follow the path of the carbon as it changes from carbon dioxide through various compounds. He used radioactive carbon and traced the path of the conversion, identifying 11 intermediate compounds created by the plant. Calvin and his assistants also made oxygen radioactive and detectable within the plant. His ultimate goal was to improve on the natural processes by which the sun's energy is changed into chemical energy and to duplicate photosynthesis in the laboratory. For this work, Calvin received the Nobel Prize in chemistry in 1961.

Calvin was born in St. Paul, Minnesota. He received a Bachelor of Science degree from the Michigan College of Mining and Technology in 1931 and his Ph.D. in 1936 from the University of Minnesota. A grant from the Rockefeller Foundation made possible two years of postgraduate study in Manchester, England,

At a 1961 White House party for Nobel Prize winners, Dr. Calvin chats with his hostess, Mrs. John F. Kennedy

under the guidance of Professor Michael Polanyi. When he returned to the United States in 1937 he was named an instructor in chemistry at the University of California, and in 1941 was promoted to assistant professor.

During World War II Calvin worked on research on military projects. A member of the scientific team which worked for the National Defense Research Council, he was also connected with the Manhattan Project, which produced the first atomic bomb. An important contribution to the war effort was his research on oxygen-carrying chelate compounds (organic substances having atoms of metal attached to them). Another notable achievement was Calvin's simple method of obtaining oxygen for industrial purposes from the air. The process was widely used in the South Pacific when regular supplies of oxygen were not available because of transport difficulties.

Calvin works in many different aspects of his field: theoretical organic chemistry, photochemistry, biochemistry and photosynthesis. He also works in bacteriology, general systems theory, biophysics and space science. Because of his special interest in biophysics, bio-astronautics and space science, he is a member of the Space Committee of the National Defense Research Council and serves as an adviser to the National Aeronautics and Space Administration.

Calvin has published hundreds of scientific papers in journals and summarized his experiments and findings in a number of books, among them *The Theory of Organic Chemistry* (1941), *Isotopic Carbon* (1949), *Chemistry of the Chelate Compounds* (1949), and *The Path of Carbon in Photosynthesis* (1957).

ERNST BORIS CHAIN
1906-

"I consider it a great honor to make a medical cure available to tens of thousands of allied troops who endangered their lives in the face of a terrible foe...I see therein the hand of fate which has brought this privilege to a member of that persecuted nation, of which millions were massacred by that same enemy. I am happy and proud to be a Jew," said Dr. Ernst Boris Chain, one of the discoverers of penicillin, when he received the Nobel Prize in 1945, in the presence of the King of Sweden, the diplomatic corps, world-famous men of science, and his companions for the prize, Sir Alexander Fleming and Sir Howard Florey.

Born in Germany, Chain's interest in science came from his father, who was a chemist and industrialist, and also a friend of Professor Chaim Weizmann, later to become the first president of the State of Israel. Chain studied chemistry and physiology in Berlin and left Germany in 1933, immediately after Hitler's rise to power. He did research at Cambridge University, then moved to Oxford University where one of his projects led the way to the discovery of penicillin.

Chain suggested to Sir Howard Florey, head pathologist at the Oxford Pathological Institute, that they investigate the molds created by micro-organisms which are able to destroy bacteria.

In studying medical bacteriological literature, Chain had come across studies on the subject by various scientists since the days of Pasteur. He chose three detailed investigations for closer research, including the famous study on *penicillium notatum* published by Professor Fleming in 1929. Chain had much background material for this project since a former scientist at the Institute had collected all types of molds, although he had not studied them in detail. This collection, rich in *penicillium notatum* cultures, was turned over to Chain. If these fungus cultures had not been available penicillin might still be waiting for discovery.

For years, English scientists had been trying to isolate strains produced by such cultures. Chain succeeded in isolating the material he called penicillin.

After he had produced penicillin he sought to establish its influence on bacteria. "As a chemist, I could not do this alone," he said. Chain discussed the problem with Professor Florey, who then actively participated in the experiments. Florey found that penicillin's strength was ten times greater than that of the sulphonamides, which, until then, were the most potent bacteria killers known. This encouraged him to experiment on living organisms. The first four mice infected with staphylococcus and streptococcus bacteria recovered completely overnight when they received thirty mgs. of penicillin. Four other mice which did not receive the penicillin died the next day. This was remarkable because the huge dose of thirty mgs. had no toxic effects.

Dr. Chain (left) greets other delegates to a 1963 "Special Assembly on Man's Right to Freedom From Hunger" at the United Nation's Food and Agriculture Organization headquarters in Rome

Today we know that the success of this experiment was due to the fact that penicillin belongs to the dipeptide family which, unlike other chemical substances, is free of all poison. The non-toxicity to humans, established in 1941, was Chain's and Florey's most important gift to science.

Their discovery was published in the weekly medical journal *Lancet,* which appears every Friday. "The next day," reported Chain, "Fleming called us at the Institute from London and said that he had heard we had found something interesting in his *penicillium notatum.* He asked permission to see it. He came, saw it, and left. After that I did not see him until we were awarded the Nobel Prize jointly."

After he left Oxford, Chain became the director of the International Research Center for Chemical Microbiology in Rome, from 1949 to 1960. He was then appointed professor of biochemistry, at London University. He will be remembered as one of the discoverers of penicillin whose work fired the imagination of the scientific world and spurred research that resulted in the discovery of other important antibiotic substances.

Having pioneered in the isolation of penicillin, Dr. Chain, shown in his Oxford laboratory in 1944, worked on the problem of manufacturing the "miracle" drug synthetically

PAUL EHRLICH
1854-1915

Scientists have long known that the body attempts to protect itself against certain diseases by creating antibodies to fight bacteria which invade it. These antibodies are often able to immunize the body against further attack by these bacteria. But the process of isolating these antibodies and inducing their production so that use could be made of them was slow and time-consuming work. What a triumph it would be if scientists could synthesize — or artificially create — such antibodies for specific bacteria which ravaged mankind, thought Paul Ehrlich, a German biochemist and bacteriologist. Ehrlich, director of an institute for serum research at Stieglitz in 1896 (later the Institute for Experimental Therapy in Frankfurt-am-Main) undertook the task, laying the foundations for modern chemotherapy and advancing man's knowledge of immunology.

For his initial experiments, Ehrlich chose a microscopic parasite called trypanosome, which is transmitted easily from body to body and is relatively large. He developed a vaccine containing the parasite and injected it into the blood of stricken animals. The vaccine killed all the bacteria, but the laboratory animals died because of the toxic effects of the vaccine. Ehrlich continued to experiment until he found a suitable chemical called benzoporphyrin. He selected two sick rats and injected one of them with the new chemical. The bacteria were destroyed in the rat which received an injection and the animal recovered. But the untreated rat died. This vaccine was the first artificial antibody to affect the cause of a disease without harming the recipient animal.

Ehrlich then tackled the task of developing a vaccine for syphilis, a highly contagious disease which plagued mankind for ages. After years of experiments and refinements Ehrlich tested his new compound, Salvarsan 606, on human patients and the chemical was discovered to be extremely effective. (Salvarsan means "the vaccine that saves" and 606 stands for the number of experiments conducted in the vaccine's development.) Not only scientists but the entire world rejoiced that a treatment had finally been found for the dreaded disease. In addition, a significant breakthrough had been

Erlich examining one of his experiments

made in the field of immunology. Ehrlich was awarded the 1908 Nobel Prize in Physiology and Medicine, which he shared with Elie Metchnikoff. Despite its many benefits, Salvarsan 606 was found to be toxic in many cases and Ehrlich and his assistants developed a less toxic vaccine, which they called Neosalvarsan.

Ehrlich also made substantial contributions to the fields of hematology, cellular pathology, the use of dyes in microscopy, and the study of other diseases, including cancer. When he died, he was eulogized by his countryman and colleague, Emil von Behring, discoverer of the diphtheria vaccine and a 1901 Nobel winner as "one of the most noble figures of experimental therapeutic research... king of the branch of science" founded by Ehrlich and the creator of a new school in medical research.

ALBERT EINSTEIN
1879-1955

In the development of technology, a few great men stand out whose ideas have changed the course not only of science but of history. Outstanding among these is Dr. Albert Einstein.

Einstein was born in Germany to a middle-class Jewish family who moved to Munich while he was still a young boy. Albert went to school in that anti-Semitic city — the only Jewish boy in his class, and was endlessly tormented by his classmates. He vowed never to wear a German uniform and when he was called up for German military service, he begged his parents to leave the country. Because they were Jews, his father's business had also been suffering, so they abandoned their German citizenship and moved to Italy. From there Albert applied to enter the Zurich Technical Institute. He passed the tests in physics and mathematics with distinction, but failed miserably in languages, botany and zoology. He was refused entrance, but recognizing his rare gifts in mathematics and physics, his examiners recommended a teacher to help him in the other subjects. At 17 he again took the examination and was accepted at the Institute.

The family could not afford to support their student son and years of hardship and poverty followed. As soon as he had finished his studies, Albert set out to find work as a science teacher. But everywhere he met with obstacles. He was stateless and a Jew. Only through the help of a friend was he able to find work as an examiner of patents in the Zurich Patent Office, an employment much beneath his capacities. But this did not stifle his inquiring mind and during office hours he pondered over problems of physics.

In 1905 he published the famous article on the theory of relativity in a scientific journal, which caused a storm of excitement throughout the scientific world. He was immediately offered a professorship at the Zurich university and another at the University of Prague, which he took. He also accepted the post of head of a new physics laboratory (requested by the Kaiser), but on the condition that he would never have to become a German citizen. By the age of 35 he was director of the department.

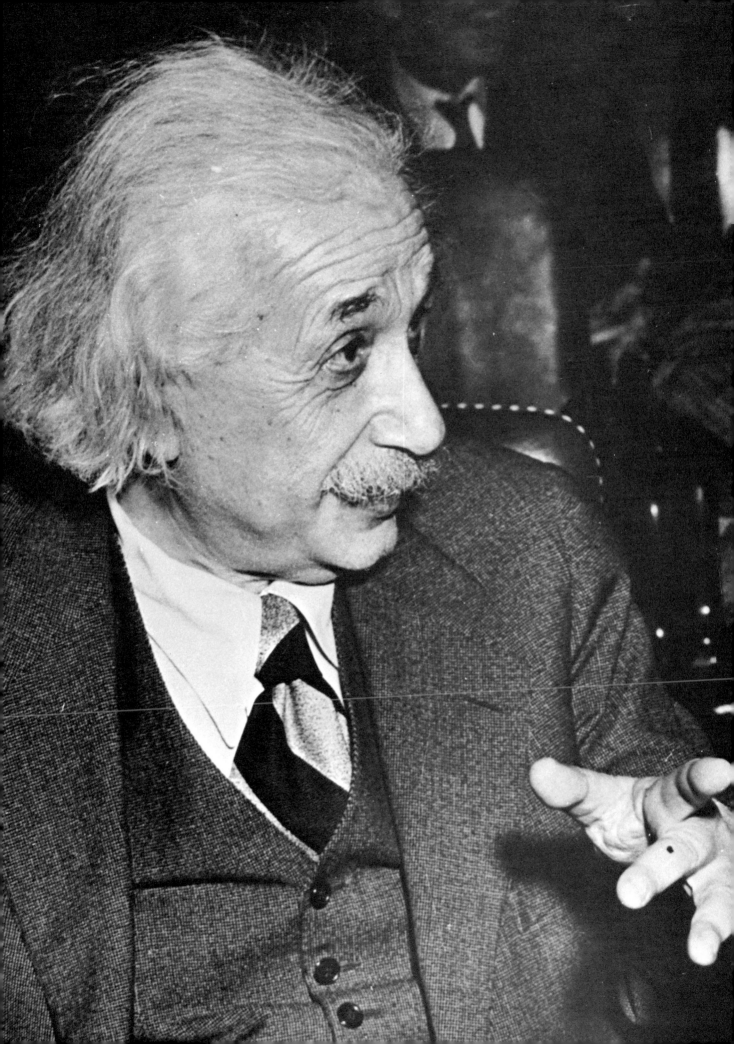

Einstein's theory of relativity forced people to revise many of the concepts they had about the nature of time and space. His theories paved the way for advances in atomic physics, although he was one of the few who realized what horror they could bring.

He was awarded the Nobel Prize for Physics in 1921, and

Prof. Einstein with President Warren Harding

Dr. Einstein shares a joke with Rabbi Stephen S. Wise (center) and late New York Mayor Fiorello H. LaGuardia

although he was by then world famous, he remained a deeply modest man. His main interests, outside of his scientific work, were pacifism and Zionism. He toured America, lecturing for the United Jewish Appeal, appearing with Weizmann, and other eminent Zionist leaders.

"Zionism to me is not only the problem of founding agricultural settlements. The Jewish people are alive, therefore the Jewish national feeling must be developed everywhere. The building of Eretz Israel is not a matter of patronage for us or of immigration. It is the most important problem of the Jewish people. In the building of the land, the feeling of Jewish solidarity which is just now awakening will find its real object."

In 1933, Einstein's house was raided by the Nazis and a price was put on his head. He settled in the United States, became an American citizen in 1940, and worked as professor of theoretical physics at the Princeton University Institute of Advanced Study.

After the death of Weizmann, Einstein was asked if he would run for election as President of Israel. He refused, knowing that he was not a man of the political world. He became trustee of the Hebrew University and donated to it his manuscripts on the *Theory of Relativity*.

On August 2, 1939, Einstein, urged by six other eminent physicists, wrote President Franklin D. Roosevelt his famous letter urging him to encourage study of the atom and the development of a new kind of bomb that was to change the course of history.

Until his death, Einstein continued giving his knowledge to the free world, urging it to beware of the terrible dangers inherent in the atom bomb, spurring it on to find a deterrent to hatred and bigotry, helping and trying to teach it that love of mankind is the vital goal of life.

RICHARD FEYNMANN
1918-

Waves of rapidly moving electrons emanating from radioactive materials presented physicists with a new force in atomic energy, completely different from a second force called the "strong intermediate force," which holds the nucleus of an atom together. Physicists of the 1950's called the new find the "weak intermediate force" in order to distinguish it from its predecessor. Richard Feynmann worked on setting down the law by which the weak intermediate force works, and in 1957 developed a theory which states that it is dependent on the various qualities of the particles. This was a vital contribution to the understanding of the nucleus of the atom.

Richard Feynmann attributes his interest in nature to his father. The two went together on long trips through forests, and his father would explain the various phenomena they encountered. "Father taught me the attraction and harmony of the world of nature," Feynmann said. "He did not know anything for sure — such as whether a certain insect had eight legs or 100, but he understood everything." The youth's interest was aroused, and he became fascinated with the workings of nature. Richard was not an attentive student, and spent much of his time in class chatting with friends. Then one day, a teacher shoved a book into his hands and told him not to open his mouth until the book was finished. "This was how I learned mathematics," Feynmann related.

He completed his studies at Princeton, and during World War II headed a group working at the Los Alamos laboratories, dealing with theoretical calculations related to the development of the atom bomb. He was also present at the historic first bomb test in the Alamogordo desert in July 1945.

In Stockholm in 1965 when he received the Nobel Prize in Physics, Feynmann concluded his speech with a question: "What ever happened to the Quantum Theory that I loved in my youth? It seems to have aged over the years and young people no longer find anything worthwhile in it, although one can say the best that can be said of old things — it was a good mother who gave birth to good children." Within a few years, three scientists, including

Feynmann (working at the California Institute of Technology), began to work on changing the electrodynamics of the quantum. The three worked individually during 1947-48, with no contact between them, and corrected the theory. With the corrections, the electrodynamics of the quantum became a useful tool no longer to be ignored in the study of basic elementary materials. Every physicist who deals with these materials uses the new theory, and the diagrams, named after Feynmann, make the work much easier.

King Gustaf Adolf presents Prof. Feynman with his prize during the 1965 Nobel ceremonies

There are those who claim that many artificial links still exist in the revised theory, that it is perfectly presentable mathematically but that there are still phenomena whose existence, from the physicists' point of view, are not properly explained. But regardless of what future discoveries will reveal about his theory, there is no question that it contributed mightily to the science of quantum electrodynamics.

JAMES FRANCK
1882-1964

In June, 1945, James Franck suggested that American scientists conduct a series of atomic experiments in front of representatives of all the nations of the world. Franck, a distinguished scientist himself, was convinced that the sight of the most dangerous weapons known to man would deter even the most war-bent advisers and statesmen. His suggestion was not accepted by the Pentagon, but his prediction that if atomic weapons were tested indiscriminately, there would be an armaments race with unforeseeable results, came true.

This was not the first time Franck had played the role of prophet. He was one of the small but important group of Jewish scientists, uprooted from Nazi Germany and scattered throughout the laboratories of America, whose work contributed so much to the Allied victory in World War II. Franck early recognized the implications of Hitler's rise to power, and resigned from his post at the University of Gottingen where he had served as Professor of Experimental Physics and head of the Physics Institute since 1920. His research there into atomic structure had won him the Nobel Prize in 1925, which he shared with his colleague Dr. Gustav Hertz. He also had come to the attention of Dr. Niels Bohr, who suggested that he accept a position at the University of Copenhagen in Denmark.

By 1935 Franck had joined a stream of Jewish scientists emigrating to America, many of whom became associated with the great Albert Einstein. These men knew the extent of German research into the structure of the atom, and wanted to prevent Germany from developing atomic weapons of war. With their personal experience of Nazi pogroms, they tried to alert the American public and mobilize American military and economic might so the Nazi horror could be fought.

Franck's mission in this endeavor was to acquaint U.S. leaders with the potentialities of atomic energy both for war and for peace. None knew the German scientific and military establishment better than Franck He had studied at the University of Berlin, and had

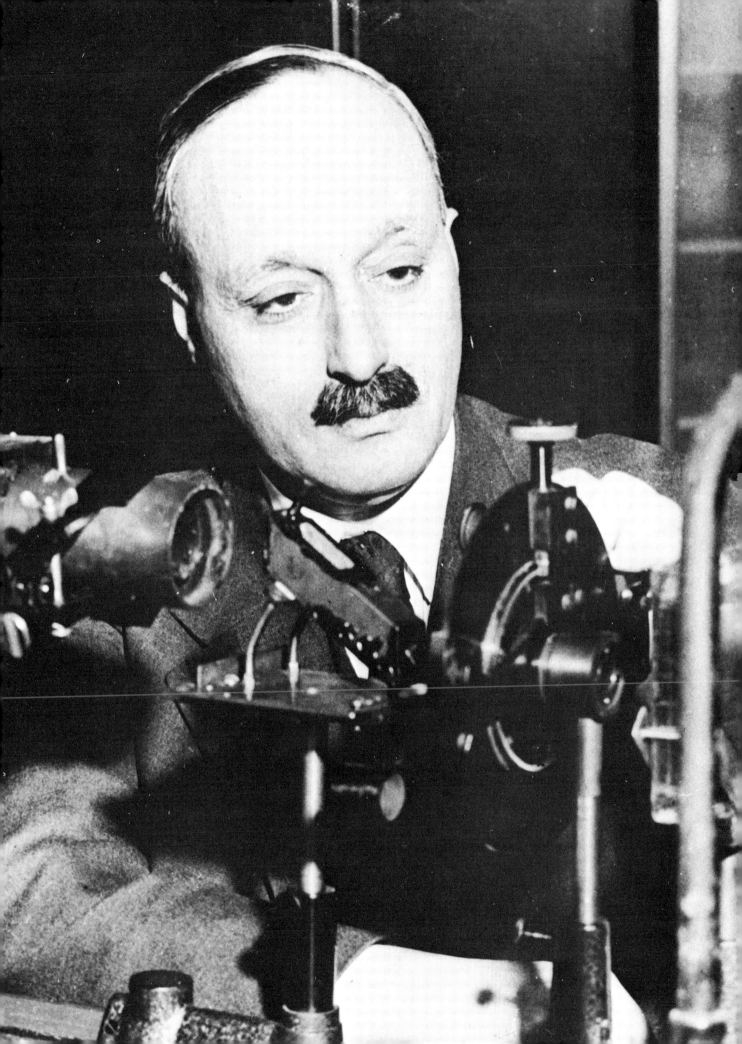

served in the German Army during World War I, winning the Iron Cross. He headed the Department of Physical Chemistry at Kaiser Wilhelm Institute, as center of atomic research, and was awarded the Nobel Prize for his discovery of the laws governing the behavior of electrons within the atom. This honor had come to him in the twenties, years before most people had even conceived of atomic energy. In America Franck continued his nuclear research, both at Johns Hopkins University in Baltimore and at the University of Chicago

But there was another aspect to Franck's career, This was his investigation into the mysteries of photosynthesis, the marvelous process by which green plants utilize sunlight to produce carbohydrates from water and carbon dioxide. All living things depend on this process for their food supply, either directly as do plants, or, in the case of humans or animals who eat the plants, indirectly.

In 1949 Dr. Franck was made head of the American Society of Plant Physiologists. His sponsors noted the privilege of having their research directed and their findings coordinated by the leading authority in the field. The receipt of this honor stimulated him to further research, which he summarized in a major part of the book *Photosynthesis in Plants*. The German government, anxious to make amends for the Nazi period, also conferred honors upon him through his former university, Gottingen. But a tribute far greater awaited him, when, together with his friend Albert Einstein, he received the honorary degree of Doctor of Science from the Technion in Haifa, Israel. Here was an institute of the physical sciences after his own heart, its aim not war, but the welfare of mankind.

ALFRED HERMANN FRIED
1864-1921

His intuition and logic told him that a world war was impending and so he dedicated his life to its prevention. At the turn of the century and in the prime of his life, Alfred Hermann Fried channeled all his strength toward this one goal. In 1909 his book, *The Sick War,* appeared, containing his views of militarism, which was already on the rise in Germany and the Austro-Hungarian Empire. He also wrote on international law, established a peace movement, and edited a magazine which fought for an international peace organization. His was a totally new concept, that of a united Europe. This solidarity was absolutely necessary for peace, according to Fried. He felt that economic factors were paving the way to a united Europe, if only war could be averted.

In 1892, Fried founded the first union for peace in Germany. He worked assiduously with German experts on international law and traveled from one country to another, participating in international peace congresses. In 1907 he came to the United States to study the Pan-American movement. He felt that an international organization to maintain peace was of primary importance.

> "It is possible to solve every dispute peacefully, but there must be the desire to do so, and this desire will be created only if a marked change in the basic nature of nations takes place. These changes will occur only under the influence of hard facts... I again claim: the logic of life will be our salvation."

Alfred Nobel did not think highly of Fried's peace efforts. He wrote Bertha Von Suttner, Austrian pacifist and Fried's colleague:

> "To ask for disarmament is to make yourself utterly ridiculous without gaining anything... My factories for munitions and explosives will perhaps succeed in bringing an end to war more quickly than all your meetings. When two opposing army divisions can destroy one another

within a few seconds, there is no doubt that every civilized nation will shake with fear and will abandon its army."

Nobel did not live long enough to see the mistake he was making, but his words were typical of the atmosphere in which Fried had to conduct his hopeless battle. His efforts, however, did not go unnoticed by the world, and in 1911 he was awarded the Nobel Peace Prize.

Two of Fried's most important books were *The Problem of Disarmament* (1905), and *Pan-America, A Handbook for the Peace Movement,* (two volumes, 1911-1913). These two works contain rich and at times extraordinary historical and statistical material, such as the yearly military expenditures of several European states; detailed reports on international peace organizations and peace committees in The Hague formed at the behest of the Russian Czar; and international law problems. In the second volume, some 260 pages were devoted to the history of the idea of peace from the Bible to Immanuel Kant.

On August 11, 1914, during the first weeks of World War I, Fried wrote in his diary:

"Everyone pities me. 'Poor Fried!' is heard everywhere. What a perversion of our work this compassion is! As if we did everything because we thought the outbreak of the war could easily be prevented; and then, when war came, all our efforts had been in vain. This was beyond our influence, they think. But the opposite was the basis of our work. Specifically because it was clear to us that war still presented a danger, because we knew that a war in Europe would be a war of the world, we worked as we did, to act as an obstacle to war.

That war did break out does not prove that we were wrong, but that we were right. It is not 'poor Fried,' but rather 'poor people,' who did not back the solution. that we presented to them."

Fried went to Switzerland during the war, but returned to his native Vienna after Versailles, but his pacifist journal was closed down. With his income cut off, he ended his life in a poorhouse.

DONALD ARTHUR GLASER
1926-

The winner of the 1960 Nobel Prize for Physics, Donald A. Glaser, was the inventor of the bubble chamber. What is a bubble chamber? According to Dr. Glaser, it is "a pressure cooker with windows," but it constituted a considerable step forward in the pursuit of atomic research, for it permits scientists to photograph the movements of the smallest particles of the atom. In the bubble's atmosphere of highly heated gas, the particles can be photographed. Use of the bubble chamber led to the discovery of new particles and to further experimentation in the field of atomic research. The bubble quickly earned a respected place among the rich collection of apparatuses in use at the physics laboratories of the University of California's Berkeley campus, as well as at most other experimental physics centers.

Glaser's work began in 1952 when he found that existing instruments for measuring the paths of atomic particles — notably the photographic emulsion and Wilson's cloud chamber — were neither adequate nor accurate. Their limits became more obvious when scientists managed to free atomic particles with million-volt charges. Glaser then created a one-inch "bubble chamber." The bubble failed in its first test, but further experiments, using highly heated propane gas, succeeded. The gas, held under great pressure to prevent boiling and vaporization, was capable of revealing and retaining the paths of moving particles discharged by atoms while photographs of the paths were made. This enabled scientists to carefully study the components of the atom.

The original bubble chamber, however, permitted study only of charged particles. In 1956 Glaser began using another type of condensed gas, which allowed him to photograph neutral particles as well. At the same time, the size of the chambers used grew. The largest was 72 inches long, and gave scientists a new observation point for the accurate and rapid study of the atom. The present Berkeley bubble chamber photographs atomic tracks every 14 seconds, taking three pictures at a time, giving stereoscopic views. In

one experiment, Glaser and his aides examined 16,000 such photographs.

Before Glaser's invention, scientists could not follow subatomic action, which takes place in a billionth of a second. Knowledge of this action was absolutely necessary, however, if scientists were ever to find out what really takes place in the atom, which contains almost all of the known types of cosmic energy, and is in effect a microcosm of the universe. Glaser's invention corrected many of the shortcomings of the two conventional instruments used before 1952 — the photographic emulsion and Wilson's cloud chamber — while incorporating their advantages.

The young professor-inventor was born in the United States, the son of a Jewish immigrant from Russia. After receiving his B.S. degree in 1946, he did graduate work at the California Institute of Technology. In 1949 he was appointed instructor in physics at the University of Michigan, and rose rapidly in the academic world. In 1953 he was promoted to assistant professor, in 1955 to associate professor, and two years later — when he was only 31 years old — to full professor. In 1960 he was named professor in the famed physics department of the University of California, where he constructed his largest bubble chamber to date.

FRITZ HABER
1868–1934

Nearly all of the discoveries of the great Jewish chemist, Fritz Haber, were made with an eye toward helping his native Germany — in peacetime and in war. And yet, with the rise of Nazism, Haber was forced to flee from his homeland, a despised man. He died soon after his flight, and mercifully never lived to see to what horrible ends his work was to be put by the Nazi regime.

Haber's greatest discovery was a way to produce ammonia gas from a mixture of nitrogen and hydrogen. This gas is of basic importance in the manufacture of chemical fertilizers. An ammonia and soda factory bought his process in 1926 and, as a result, expanded at such a fantastic rate that within five years it became the largest such factory in Germany. As a result of Haber's process Germany's economy was enriched by a million marks. The method resulted in a marked increase in agricultural output at a time when Germany was sorely in need of food. One acre of land fertilized with a pound of fertilizer made from Haber's ammonia produced three times the usual harvest of wheat, potatoes and celery. This great aid to agriculture earned Haber the Nobel Prize for Chemistry in 1918, as well as numerous honorary doctorates from universities in Germany and Sweden.

In 1911, Haber was already working to organize an important science center in Germany, with money lent to him by a Berlin banker. The center was set up in the suburbs of Berlin and was opened in 1912 by Kaiser Wilhelm, after whom it was named. The center sprawled over a large tract of land and included 12 large laboratories for private research work. Haber himself worked in the laboratories, and before long he presented the world with an alarm to warn of escaping gases before explosions and subsequent loss of life could occur.

At the beginning of World War I, Haber volunteered for active duty and fought on the front. Before long he was called back to serve on a more important front: the fight for raw materials for the manufacture of ammunition. Haber and Emil Rathenau, both

Prof. Haber in the library of his home

German Jews, found that the German leaders had neglected to provide means for acquiring the raw materials necessary to run the war. The Allied forces were cordoning off Germany and trying to choke her into submission, not permitting materials to arrive from Chile. Haber succeeded in extracting nitrogen from the air in order to make gun powder. His experiments also advanced the possibilities for gas warfare, which actually started on April 22, 1915, when metal containers gave off clouds of chloroform, which rose four miles high and spread half a mile wide. As a result, the front line of the Allied forces, until then impregnable, broke. But Haber was not satisfied, because winds affected the stream of gas and presented potential trouble. He introduced gas shells, which could be fired from cannons. Haber not only advanced gas warfare, but prepared Germany's defense against it. At a much later date his findings contributed to the development of insecticides for use in agriculture.

After Germany's defeat, Haber tried to find ways in which to help rebuild his homeland. He attempted to extract gold and silver from sea water in order to lighten the financial burden of payments imposed by the Allied countries after the war, and he did succeed to some extent. But the cost of extracting the gold exceeded its value, so he abandoned the project.

In 1924 Haber decided to make a world tour and was welcomed everywhere as a renowned scientist. He spent a few months in Japan as the guest of the wealthy industrialist, Hu Shih. Together they founded a German-Japanese Institute for developing cultural-scientific ties.

As both a person and a scientist, Fritz Haber did great things for his ungrateful homeland, Germany. Few Germans were more attached to their homeland than he. It is ironic that the most anti-Semitic force in modern history was unwittingly aided by this well-meaning, ingenious Jew.

PAUL HEYSE
1830-1914

Paul Heyse, the first German author to win the Nobel Prize for literature, is noted for his masterful, realistic style of writing which found expression in the fields of poetry, drama, the novel, and short stories. Heyse admired Goethe, classical literature and elegant style, placing a great deal of value on form itself. In his long life he passed through numerous creative stages, but his artistic goal remained essentially the same: he constantly strived for stylistic perfection.

Though Heyse composed over fifty dramas, he knew little about the drama of life itself or the problems of ordinary people. His work suffers from the fact that he remained unexposed to varied experiences, keeping very much to his own circle of friends and acquaintances, unaware of the anguish of the oppressed. Therefore, his heroes tend to resemble their author in their lack of comprehension of poverty and suffering.

Even his finest work, the story of L'*Arrabbiata* (The Fury) with its perfect composition and characterizations and vivid description of the sea, avoids the essential problems of life, concentrating rather on style. However, a few works reveal deep feeling, such as the truly heartrending *Toten Lieder,* poems he wrote on the death of his children.

In the mid-1800's there was a critical struggle in literature between realism and romanticism and some writers and poets of the period incorporated elements of both. After 1870 when the creative force in German literature began to weaken, Paul Heyse continued in the tradition which combined classicism and romanticism.

When Heyse was 82 years of age he was awarded the Nobel Prize in the spirit of Alfred Nobel's stipulation that it be awarded for "a work of idealistic character."

At that time he had already been elected an honorary citizen of Munich and had been given numerous other awards and distinctions. Many professors of literature in the German universities were interested in having the international prize go to the elderly and esteemed writer. Among them was Carl David Af

Viergen, Permanent Secretary of the Nobel Prize Committee and an enthusiastic admirer of Heyse. In his letter of recommendation he wrote, "Germany has not had a genius such as this since the days of Goethe. Heyse's short stories are paragons of perfection."

Heyse was the most versatile and perhaps the most important writer of the later romantic school. His output runs the entire gamut of *belles-lettres* — plays, novels, short stories and poetry. His novels, usually dealing with people of the social elite, treat problems of love and marriage with deep psychological insight, and always with a masterful style. He is able to say much in a few words; his composition is impeccable and his dialogue dramatic. His short stories also, with their superb technical finish, are enduring and have assured him a place in the literature of the twentieth century.

ARTHUR KORNBERG
1918-

The term, "genetic control" describes what could be the most revolutionary scientific achievement of all time. It refers to the possibility of man changing the character and nature of human beings through predetermining the characteristics they will inherit. If science finally achieves that goal, it will be due in large measure to the original research done by Arthur Kornberg, an American-Jewish scientist, who was awarded the Nobel Prize in 1959 for his work in isolating DNA, the basic living factor in cells. This marked the 14th time that a Jewish research scientist had been so honored.

Kornberg's parents, poor immigrants from Galicia, gave the boy a good education, and he proved an excellent student even though he had to work nights to help pay his way through school. In 1941 he received his medical diploma from the University of Rochester. During World War II, he worked in the public service division of the National Institute of Health in Bethesda, Maryland, where he decided to study the factors within the body which cause its chemical activities. The most advanced work in biochemistry was then being done at New York University Medical School, so Kornberg went there to work under the outstanding Spanish researcher, Dr. Severo Ochua.

The two scientists found a way to extract enzymes which participate in the synthesis of nucleic acids from a living cell, which in turn determine our inherited characteristics. Dr. Kornberg studied the enzymes from which DNA — deoxyribonucleic acid — is formed. DNA is a protein necessary for the reproduction of cells. He freed one of the enzymes by using high frequency sound waves. Afterwards, he purified the enzyme by chemical means and mixed it with thiamin, one of the four basic components of DNA. After years of work, he succeeded in creating DNA synthetically. Meanwhile, Dr. Ochua was doing similar work with RNA — ribonucleic acid — which works along with DNA.

The work of Arthur Kornberg is paving the way for man to influence hereditary characteristics, which until now were thought to be in the hands of Nature alone.

SIR HANS KREBS
1901-

The Jewish scientist, Sir Hans Krebs, was awarded the Nobel Prize for Physics in 1953, along with a second German Jew, Dr. Fritz Lipmann. As young men the two Jewish researchers were appointed to the staff of the Kaiser Wilhelm Institute in the outskirts of Berlin. Both were dismissed from German universities when Hitler rose to power. Krebs was invited to Cambridge where he "arrived with almost nothing, outside of a few belongings and a valise full of books", as he once related. Lipmann settled in the United States and was appointed a professor at Harvard. Three thousand miles apart, the two scientists uncovered two important secrets of nature: how living organisms change food into energy, and how they use food for growth. It was for this work that they were awarded the Nobel Prize.

Krebs, born in Heildesheim, decided that he would become a doctor like his father. He studied at many universities in Germany (Göttingen, Freiburg, Munich and Berlin) and received his degree from Hamburg in 1925. The talented youth did not show any interest in practical medicine however, and went into research. A year later, after completing advanced studies in chemistry, the famous Jewish-German scholar, Professor Otto Heinrich Warburg, invited him to serve as his assistant at the Kaiser Wilhelm Institute. It was Warburg who suggested that young Krebs and Lipmann work together, 20 years before they received the Nobel Prize.

Krebs worked under Warburg until 1930. When the Nazis came to power he was discharged from his position as lecturer at the University of Freiburg's School of Medicine. The young researcher had earned a good name in the scientific world and was invited to continue his work at Cambridge. There, with the aid of a Rockefeller Fund fellowship, he continued his studies and research. For two years he worked for one of the most famous scholars of our time, Sir Frederick Goland Hopkins, professor of biochemistry and recipient of the 1929 Nobel Prize for his work with vitamins. While Hopkins' protégé in the field of biochemistry, Krebs received an M.S. degree from Cambridge.

Krebs receives the Nobel Prize from King Gustav II of Sweden

The University of Sheffield then invited Krebs to lecture there. He served in this position from 1935 to 1938, at which time he was made lecturer in biochemistry and head of the entire department. *Nature,* Britain's scientific journal, noted that Krebs was a magnetic force who attracted researchers not only from Europe but from America as well. In recognition of his scientific activities, Krebs was granted British citizenship, at the beginning of World War II, a time when Germans were in great disfavor in England. The scholar showed his appreciation with a unique contribution. He turned his attention to the problem of nutrition during wartime, and developed a special recipe for bread which provided all the nutrients required by the body. At the end of the war, Krebs was appointed professor of biochemistry and director of medical research, dealing with the exchange of materials in the human body.

Until the 18th century, man had no way of doing physical work other than with the force of his own muscles, yet no one knew how muscular energy was generated. Krebs contributed greatly to research efforts in this field by explaining how food is changed into energy. In order to describe precisely the process that transforms sugar into energy-releasing molecules, he charted the chemical composition of 20 to 30 energy molecules which had some connection with sugar. He hoped to determine which of them was able to change its composition on its own power. Two acids met the requirements, and he found that at the time of oxidation, the acid changed to a chemical "retaining wall" called acetyl co-enzyme A. After oxidation other acids were created in a chain reaction until another molecule of co-enzyme A took on a new form. As a result of this process energy was formed.

Although Krebs and Lipmann worked thousand of miles apart, the results of their research were complementary to a certain degree, and they were therefore awarded the Nobel Prize jointly. Krebs received the Lasker Prize, from the U.S. Department of Health, Education and Welfare, for his research and discoveries in the field of the body's use of food. His discoveries were of great basic impor-

Krebs at work in his laboratory

tance in understanding biological processes both in healthy and sick bodies. Krebs is a member of the "Friends of the Hebrew University." The Fund for Basic Scientific Research, set up to aid Hebrew University students who wish to take graduate work in England, is named in his honor.

LEIB DAVIDOVITCH LANDAU
1908-1968

It may very well be that the name and activity of Leib Landau, the brilliant Russian scientist, would still be unknown to many people outside of scientific circles, were it not for the automobile accident which occurred on January 7, 1962, near Moscow between 10 and 11 a.m. On that day, an unusually warm one (32 F) for one of the coldest months in Russia, a black car moved along the Dimitrov road which joined the Soviet atom center in Dubno with Moscow. The car was forced to stop suddenly. In so doing, it was thrown across the road where it jammed deep into an approaching truck. Professor Leib Landau, Soviet atomic scientist and winner of the Lenin Prize, was riding in the back seat, and it was only by a miracle that he was saved from instant death.

Forty minutes after the accident, Landau was on the operating table in Municipal Hospital No. 50 in Moscow. After examining him, the medical team did not require any special consultation in order to give the prognosis to its spokesman, Professor Grashchenko, head of the neuro-surgical department of the hospital. He announced, "There are enough injuries for one man to die four times over." The seven broken ribs — four on the right side and three on the left (out of 24) — could be treated, but what about the other injuries? They included multiple pelvic fractures and were extremely serious. Such fractures can be mortally dangerous if the sharp ends of the bones pierce the bladder, the intestines or other internal organs. A tear in Landau's pleura was also an especially critical injury. A skull fracture, with concussion and hemorrhaging in different parts of the brain, was liable to cause damage to Landau's memory. Shock could bring disturbances in the nervous system. Another danger: a lack of blood flowing to the brain. It was clear to the doctors who had bent over Landau that "the entire body was damaged" and that it was not within human power to save such a man from death.

But one thing was clear to the head of the government of the U.S.S.R. "This man must not die!" ordered Khrushchev in a telephone call to hospital authorities. And oddly enough, the man did not die.

Faced with a condition of almost certain death, the doctors prepared to fill the leader's order. The superhuman struggle against death began immediately. A whole fleet of airplanes began to move all over the world — to London, Canada and elsewhere. Medicines which were not available in Russia were brought in. Specialists were summoned from Sweden, France and Britain for emergency consultation. Naturally, a permanent watch of the best Soviet specialists was set up by Landau's bedside. In all 80 doctors, among them half a dozen internationally known ones, were called to treat Landau. This army of foreign doctors was doubtful whether the physicians of Hospital No. 50 could save the life of the scientist. But the words of Khrushchev reverberated in their ears: "Save him!"

If there are miracles in the world of medicine, this case is one of them, for Professor Landau, believed to be mortally injured and beyond healing, was not only brought back to life, but his mental faculties restored. His brain had been full of pus and dangerously swollen. Complete disorganization of the nervous system had occurred, and his pulse had stopped beating. No less than four times, "clinical death" was determined. His recovery was considered a sort of "resurrection."

His father, one of the few Jews accepted as students by the University of Moscow, was an engineer. The son inherited his abilities, and at the age of 18 had already published an important scientific report. He desired to continue his studies abroad, and although his teachers warmly recommended him as one of the shining physicists of the Soviet Union, travel was difficult. In 1929, the German-Jewish scientist, Max Born (who later received the Nobel Prize for Physics) was impressed by Landau and expressed the desire to add him to his group of students. Thus (with the help of an American fund) he went for specialized training in Europe. In Göttingen, he studied with Born, in Leipzig with Heisenberg, in Copenhagen with Niels Bohr, in Oxford with Sir Ernest Rutherford. All of them were recipients of the Nobel Prize for Physics. Later, he studied with Pauli, a Swedish Jew, in Zurich. In 1931 he returned to Russia. Three years later, he received his doctorate in physics and only one year afterward was appointed professor at the Academy of Kharkov. Within a short time he was asked to head the Physics Institute in Moscow. In 1937 he was arrested, accused of spying for Germany and sentenced to ten years' imprisonment. He was released in 1939.

At the end of the 1930's, Kapitsa, a Russian scientist who had specialized in the West for a long time, had determined that liquid helium becomes nonfluid at a temperature of absolute zero. Scientists could not explain this interesting phenomenon. But in 1941 Landau gave a brilliant theoretical explanation for the nonfluidity of helium 2 (the isotope of helium), and he forecast that it would be possible to transmit two sound waves of different frequencies in liquid helium. This is the phenomenon that is called "the second sound." Some time later, the Soviet physicist Vassili Pashkov confirmed by experiment that Landau's theory is correct.

It is impossible to list briefly all the theories that this outstanding scientist developed. He published more than 120 papers, including many which he wrote together with his student and friend, Professor Yevni Lipschitz, covering basic problems of theoretical physics. His books, translated into many languages, serve as guides for physicists the world over.

Leib Landau was a member of six academies (in Russia, Denmark, Holland, England, and two in the United States). Three times he won the Russian Government prize. In 1960 he was given the Max Planck Prize; in 1962 he received the Lenin Prize and the Nobel Prize for physics.

KARL LANDSTEINER
1868-1943

Today the lives of sick or injured persons who have lost a great deal of blood can be saved by blood transfusion. Formerly, when doctors attempted to use this method, death often resulted, and the procedure was therefore abandoned. The fact that we can now save so many lives by this means must be credited to the Jewish doctor, Karl Landsteiner, who discovered the important principle of "blood types", which was to make successful blood transfusions possible.

Albumin is the nutritive protein substance contained in the blood plasma. If the albumin of one living being is injected into the body of another, the host body may send out substances to destroy the foreign material and death may result.

As long as doctors did not know the principles and laws regulating this inner conflict, they could not detect which substance from one body coming into contact with the blood of a second body was responsible for causing death. Landsteiner devoted himself to the study of this phenomenon. He made many experiments with albumins, coloring them in order to be able to trace their progress and characteristics as they fought with the host body's blood. Landsteiner proved that indiscriminate blood transfusions are dangerous, since one person's blood may contain materials which will destroy another individual's blood.

He found that blood albumin is not present in the same proportion in every body but that the proportion varies slightly from one individual to another. On the basis of these differing proportions, Landsteiner established four categories of blood types. He found if the blood of type A is injected into a body with type B blood, there is a clash between the two types, with resulting fever and often death. But if type A is injected into a person who also has type A, the two bloods mingle without any antagonism. This discovery made successful blood transfusions possible. Blood type does not change during an individual's lifetime, and is inherited by children according to certain genetic rules. For the important

Dr. Karl Landsteiner talks with Crown Prince Carl of Sweden before the 1930 Nobel ceremonies

discovery of blood types, Dr. Landsteiner was awarded the Nobel Prize in Physiology and Medicine in 1930.

Dr. Landsteiner had studied medicine in his native Vienna. In 1910 he was appointed Professor of Pathology at the University of Vienna and after World War I, he moved to The Hague. In 1922 he came to the United States to work at the Rockefeller Institute for Medical Research in New York City and soon became an American citizen.

In addition to his work on blood albumin, Landsteiner can take credit for another important scientific study. In 1937, while working at the Rockefeller Institute with his close aide, Dr. Alexander Solomon Wiener, Landsteiner mixed the blood of a rabbit with a small amount of monkey blood. When the mixture was analyzed, they found red cells chemically different from any cell they had ever seen before. They called the unfamiliar cells the Rh factor (after the Rhesus monkey, which had been used in their experiments). Dr. Landsteiner turned to other research matters, but Dr. Wiener, whose curiosity had been aroused, continued to study the Rh factor, which was to prove a valuable contribution to science.

For twenty years until his death, Landsteiner worked at the Rockefeller Institute. In 1939, at the age of seventy, he was officially retired, but continued in an advisory capacity at the Institute.

In addition to the Nobel Prize, Karl Landsteiner received many honors and awards. In 1926, he was given the Hans Aaronson Award and was also elected to membership in the British Royal Society, and in 1939, received the Paul Ehrlich Medal.

In his later years, when his wife developed cancer, he felt an obligation to do research on this disease. During his work a severe heart attack ended his life, and his wife, although mortally ill, outlived him.

On August 30, eight years after Landsteiner's death, Vienna immortalized her famous son's memory with a plaque on the wall

Landsteiner (third from left, left side) at Nobel presentation ceremonies in 1930

of the Wilhelmina Hospital. Only two words were inscribed on the tablet: "Karl Landsteiner."

Landsteiner's memory is revered in many places — wherever lives are saved by means of blood transfusions, wherever courts can determine blood relationships with the aid of blood type tests, and wherever men fight against disease.

JOSHUA LEDERBERG
1925-

In 1946, a 21-year-old Columbia University medical school student landed a summer job in a Yale University laboratory that changed his whole life, and set him on the road to a Nobel Prize for physiology and medicine.

Joshua Lederberg had intended to spend only his "summer vacation" working in Dr. Edward Lawrie Tatum's laboratory, but he became so engrossed in the problems he was researching with Dr. Tatum and his colleague, George Wells Beadle, that he never returned to medical school.

The three American scientists were searching for the answers to such important questions as: how do chemical substances in the chromosomes work? What are the principles governing heredity? How can genes produce changes in the structure and behavior of living creatures?

Until Lederberg's research at Stanford it was thought that bacteria were asexual and multiplied by dividing in half. But Professor Tatum and his young helper made a startling discovery: bacteria *did* have sexual lives. Lederberg found that bacteria possess a mechanism for the fusion of two organisms, and that during this fusion an exchange of genetic matter takes place. By "mating" two types of bacteria, he was able to create a third type, which showed the traits of its parents.

He later proved that it was possible to transfer a full set of chromosomes or even parts of a set from the cell of one bacterium to that of another. This process was called transduction. As a result, he was able to change the inherited characteristics of bacteria. Lederberg was awarded the Nobel Prize in 1958 for these discoveries.

Further study along these lines by Lederberg and one of his students, N. D. Zinder, led to yet another important discovery—that viruses attacking bacteria can add something to their hosts' genetic makeup. The process involves the transfer of genetic fragments by an invading virus from one bacterium to another which, if it survives the attack, may produce a new strain. This phenomenon is particularly

Dr, Lederberg at work in his laboratory at the University of Wisconsin

relevant to the problem of cancer, which is essentially a transformation of normal cells into malignant ones. Transduction provides a missing link that may enable science to reconcile the prevailing virus and mutation theories of cancer. "We hope that by studying the biochemical mechanism of bacteria we will succeed in finding some way to wipe out diseases in man which are basically hereditary, perhaps by a type of transduction," Lederberg wrote.

Clearly, the research Lederberg is pursuing on the basic hereditary processes in bacteria will have an important impact on our future knowledge and control of disease.

FRITZ ALBERT LIPMANN
1899-

Lipmann's unorthodox experiment on doves' liver led to the discovery of Coenzyme A, the most important element for supplying energy to the body (by changing energy from phosphate to other useful forms of chemical energy). Together with Dr. Hans Adolf Krebs, who researched the changing of food into energy in

Dr. and Mrs. Fritz Albert Lipmann dancing at the ball which is part of the Nobel Prize festivities

Dr. Lipmann (left) checks the time with other Nobel Prize winners waiting for ceremonies to begin. They are Hans Adolph Krebs, Prof. Hermann Staudinger and Prof. Fritz Zernike

the cells, Dr. Lipmann shared the Nobel Prize for medicine in 1953.

Dr. Lipmann started his work as a research scientist in the 1920's at the Kaiser Wilhelm Institute in Berlin, studying under two Nobel Prize winners, Dr. Otto Meyerhof and Dr. Albert Fischer. His research centered on the connection between energy and the exchange of materials in the body. Working with Dr. Fischer, he studied the structure of muscle tissues to probe the secrets of muscle energy, and later with the support of a Rockefeller grant, he continued his work with studies on the mechanism of phosphate.

In 1940 he proved the existence of acetyl phosphate; in 1942 he isolated it; in 1944 he was able to manufacture it. In his work on the source of energy, Dr. Lipmann developed the "dynamics of metabolism" theory. He made a study of the structure of cells affected by cancer. He solved various problems connected with pantothenic acid, an oily acid of the Vitamin B complex, found in all living tissues. He finally succeeded in isolating Coenzyme A in 1945 with his doves' liver experiment at the Massachusetts General Hospital.

Dr. Lipmann was the first to prove that Coenzyme A acts as an important factor in the production of fatty acid and steroid hormones, materials necessary to the body. Afterwards he researched the way the thyroid gland's hormones produce energy in the body. About this work, he said: "Our limited success in the investigation of this hormone's activities gives us hope that sooner or later biochemists will be able to master the mechanism of hormones in the same way that they mastered the intricacies of vitamin activities."

GABRIEL LIPPMAN
1845-1921

It is difficult to imagine what our lives would be like without color photography... the snapshots and movies we bring home from vacations, the attractive pictures we see in books and magazines, and all the advances in science and medicine made possible because we are able to take color pictures. Probably none of this would have been possible without the work of Gabriel Lippman.

Photography was not exactly "invented"; several scientists had been experimenting with the idea of "writing with light" (which is what photography means in Greek). Perhaps the two most important were Joseph Niepce of Germany, and Louis Daguerre of France who succeeded, in the early years of the 19th century, in permanently recording life images on plates covered with a chemical silver solution. Almost immediately, they dreamed of recording color as well. It was not until 1898 that French physicist Antoine Henri Becquerel (1852-1908) was able to successfully record color on film. But Becquerel's colors faded, and it took a whole generation — and Gabriel Lippman — to make them permanent.

Lippman was born in Luxemburg on August 16, 1845. He was brought to Paris at the age of 13, and there he completed his college studies. While still an undergraduate, he became interested in electrical research and wrote two scientific papers based on his own work, which deeply impressed his professors.

After serving on a scientific mission to Germany, where he worked under renowned physicists, Lippman returned to Paris and received the Doctor of Science degree from the Sorbonne in 1874.

While preparing his doctoral dissertation, he became interested in the study of electrocapillary work. Shortly after graduating from the Sorbonne, he continued his studies of this phenomenon and developed an instrument for measuring minute differences in electromotive force. This instrument is still widely in use. The importance of his discovery was such that on the basis of it alone, Lippman was elected to membership in the French Academy of Sciences.

From 1883 until his death, Lippman taught at the Sorbonne, first as a professor of mathematical physics and later as professor

Artist's conception of Lippman at work in the darkroom

of experimental physics and director of the research laboratory.

Full understanding of how Lippman produced a permanent photographic color image requires considerable background in chemistry and physics. He based his research on the wave theory of light. He placed a plate covered with a light-sensitive layer (the "film"), transparent and free from grains, in a holder which contained mercury. The mercury comes in contact with the sensitive layer during the photographic exposure, forming a chemical "mirror." After exposure, the plate is developed in the usual way. After it dries, the colors appear, seen by reflection; they remain permanent. This is due to an interference phenomenon which takes place inside the sensitive layer. During the exposure, interference occurs between the incident (direct) light rays and those reflected by the mirror, with the formation of "interference fringes" which can be measured as having half the length of a wave of light. It is these fringes which are photographically impressed within the thickness of the film. When later viewed by white light, the color is seen because at each point the plate sends back to the eye only that single color which has been impressed on it; the other colors are destroyed by "interference." The eye selects those colors which "fit into place," combining the thousands of pinpoints of color into one picture. The process has been greatly improved and sophisticated through the years, but it is still, basically, Lippman's.

In addition to his work in color photography, Lippman was responsible for many important discoveries and inventions in the fields of physics and astronomy.

In 1908, Gabriel Lippman was elected a Foreign Member of the Royal Society of London. That same year he was awarded the Nobel Prize in Physics for his discovery of the process for reproducing colors in film. On the occasion of this award, Lippman concluded his lecture with the statement: "Perhaps progress will continue. Life is short and progress is slow."

OTTO LOEWI
1873-

The problem of how a nerve activates muscles or organs was one that had long troubled scientists. Many theories had been evolved but nothing had been proven. It was generally thought that nerve fibers connected to other parts of the body, and transmitted the nerve impulse. But in 1906, T.R. Eliot came up with the idea that a chemical substance was probably involved in the functions of the nervous network. In 1907 Dixon theorized that nerves release chemicals to activate different parts of the body. Eliot and Dixon were on the right track, but it remained for Otto Loewi to show exactly what happened in the complex relationship between nerve and organ.

To do this, Loewi removed the hearts from two frogs leaving the nerves on only one of them. From this one he carefully collected the minute amount of liquid produced when the heart nerve was stimulated. He took the liquid and applied it to the second heart. As soon as the substance touched it the nerveless heart began to beat quickly. Success! The theory of the chemical transmission of nerve impulses had been proved.

Thus it was shown that a nerve does not transmit messages directly, but produces a chemical which fulfills this function. The exact material produced by the heart nerves, adrenalin, was also discovered by Otto Loewi. Through other experiments, he found the chemical substance which activates the muscular system. Others worked on different aspects of the nerve system, namely the electro-physiological elements, but the chemical explanation of nerve impulses was what interested Loewi most. For his discoveries, Loewi shared the 1936 Nobel Prize in physiology and medicine with Sir Henry Dale of England.

Otto Loewi was born in Frankfurt, Germany in 1873. After receiving an M.D. degree, he went on to study chemistry and pharmacology at the University of Marburg. His adviser, Professor H. Meir, took him from there to the University of Vienna. He was finally given a chair at the University of Graetz in 1909. There, as professor of pharmacology, he performed the experiments that led to the Nobel Prize.

In 1934 he visited America where he was invited to remain and work at the Harvard School of Medicine. Although Hitler was then on the rise to power in Germany, and the danger to Jews in Austria was clear, Loewi loved his school and his work and turned down the offer. In 1938, Germany annexed Austria. Loewi was removed from the university by the Nazis, arrested, and forced to turn over the $36,000 he had received as part of the Nobel Prize. Because of his world renown, however, various groups and individuals in England and the United States applied pressure on the Nazis, and he was eventually freed.

Sir Henry Dale, who was one of those instrumental in obtaining Loewi's freedom, made the laboratories at Oxford University avail-

Prof. Loewi (second from right) attends a Nobel Anniversary Dinner. With him (l. to r.) are Father Gannon, President of Fordham University, Nelson Rockefeller and Nobel Laureate Dr. Victor Hess (1943)

able to the Jewish scientist. A few years later the Rockefeller Foundation granted him the funds to set up a laboratory for his pharmacological experiments.

Loewi became a research professor of pharmacology at New York University's College of Medicine in 1940. A year later his wife managed to escape from Austria and joined him in New York.

Otto Loewi has always been a symbol of the patient, modest researcher. He has never been interested in publicity. Many times in his research he has come up against a blank wall, and then he puts his own instincts to use. He is well-known for his ability to decide if an experiment is worth carrying out, and if he does decide to stay with an experiment, chances are there will be positive results.

Prof. Loewi (far left) with other Nobel Prize winners at the close of the 1936 ceremonies in Sweden

ELIE METCHNIKOFF
1845-1916

"One day in my youth, when the whole family had gone to the circus, I was left alone in the house near the microscope. I looked through the lens at the live cells moving in the transparent jelly that surrounds the starfish, and wondered if similar cells in the human body act as a defense against outside attack. I thought that I was on to something extremely important and became very excited. If I had guessed correctly, a splinter of wood stuck into the jelly — which has no blood vessels or nerves — would be attacked and destroyed. And the same would happen in the finger of a man. Near our house was a fir tree, I took a few needles from it and stuck them under the transparent skin of the starfish. That night I was too excited to sleep, anticipating the results of this experiment. Early in the morning I checked, and saw that the experiment was a complete success. It served as the basis for my theory of phagocytes, the development of which absorbed the next 25 years of my life."

This is how Elie Metchnikoff described the experiment which revealed one of nature's greatest secrets to him, and which brought about a revolution in the field of medicine. Proceeding with his original insight, Metchnikoff showed that when the body is attacked by a foreign object, a regiment of protective cells immediately stages an attack on the intruder. He called these cells phagocytes or destroyer cells. If the phagocytes overcome the intruder, all is well for the body. But if the intruder is victorious, sickness or death results. He also determined that phagocytes appear on the scene only when bacteria are so strong that saliva and digestive juices cannot overcome them.

Through his research on phagocytes, Metchnikoff became interested in problems of immunization, and for his work in this area was awarded the Nobel Prize in Physiology and Medicine in 1908

After Louis Pasteur's death in 1895, Metchnikoff was appointed director of the Pasteur Institute in Paris. Hundreds of students

A rare 1909 photograph of Dr. Metchnikoff with Russian novelist Leo Tolstoy

listened to his lectures and many of them later continued along the lines he had established.

Metchnikoff was born in Odessa, Russia, the son of a Russian general and a Jewess. He emigrated as a young man to France, and years later in an interview with a Zionist journalist explained: "I attribute my great devotion to science to the fact that I am a Jew. After the murder of Alexander II, I came to the conclusion that I could not continue my research at the University of Odessa with proper concentration because the political ambitions of the students there had overcome their desire to learn." Metchnikoff recalled that

Dr, Metchnikoff in his laboratory at the Pasteur Institute, Paris

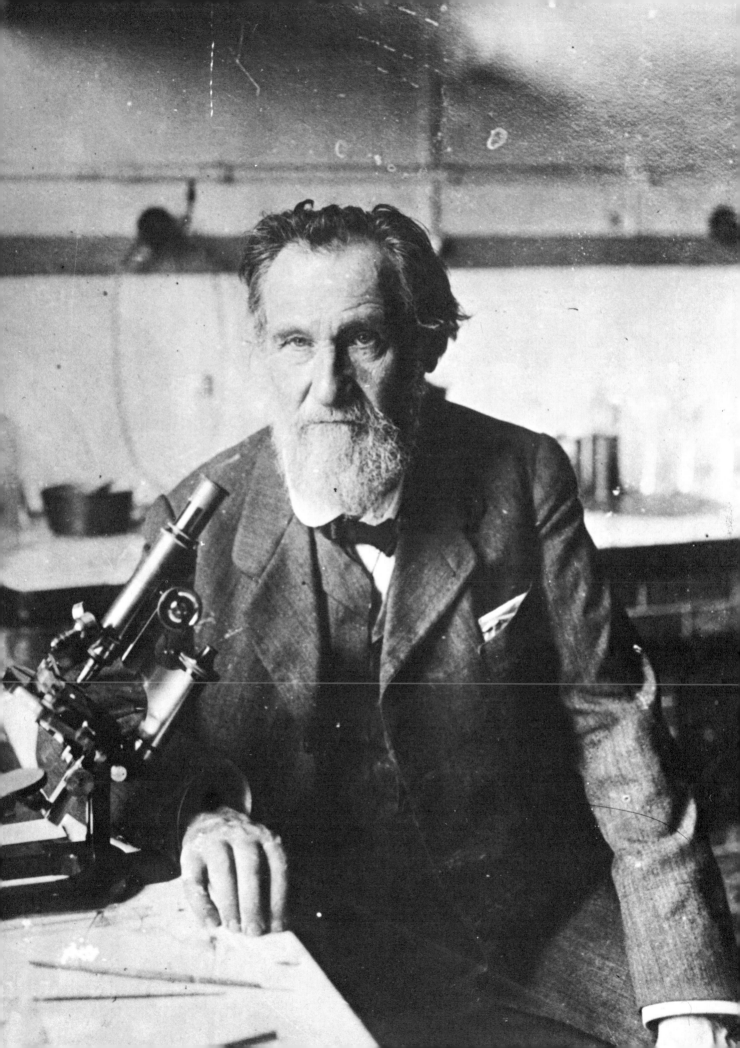

in a short time, the Russian universities lost their best scholars. Many of these men, he noted, who could have done a great deal to help Russia, were Russian Jews: "They have an abundance of vitality and energy. By their pogroms, Russia has driven away many great and talented men."

OTTO MEYERHOF
1884-1951

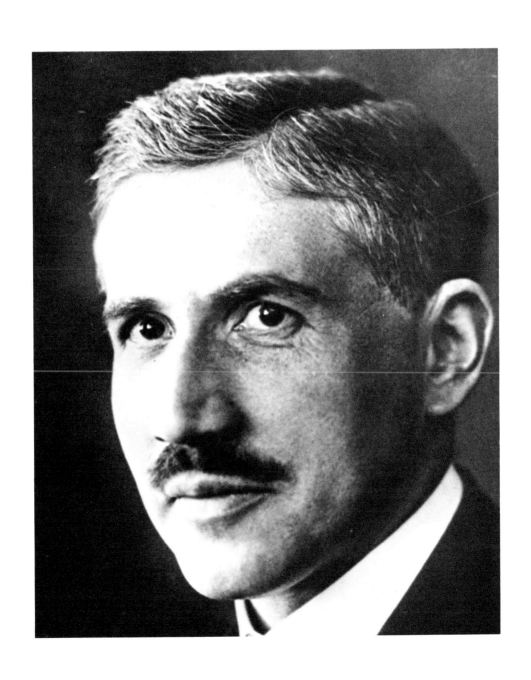

How is life created ? Can man duplicate the process of creation?

A German-Jewish scientist, Dr. Otto Meyerhof, was the first to conduct successful experiments revealing the basic processes of the living cell by means of physics and chemistry. He was awarded the Nobel Prize in 1923 for his classic study which revolutionized scientific thought and prepared the way for further studies in cell activities.

According to Meyerhof, the principles of order and existence are the same in organic and nonorganic matter. The process of development is similar for all organisms and each stage represents both a unity by itself and an inseparable part of the large unit. Atoms, the smallest particles of an element, are followed by molecules, which are groups of atoms. Large molecules, which have an existence of their own, form the end of the first stage of development and the beginning of the second. Small viruses which cause disease and chromosomes which carry heredity are part of the second stage.

Meyerhof knew that the German scientist Helmholtz had theorized that the organic source of muscle energy lies in the chemical process of food combustion in the human body. Helmholtz stated that the muscle resembles a machine and each exertion requires raw materials. Meyerhof not only identified the materials from which the human body is made, but also explained, in scientific terms, the activities and exchanges that take place there.

In many experiments on the processes and changes of energy in the muscles, he tried to define the cellular processes which use up food, by measuring the heat produced in the muscles. He made chemical analyses of frogs' muscles and found that a specific amount of glycogen (a chemical which stores sugar for the body to use during exertion) disappeared from the muscle, while oxygen was being absorbed. Carbon dioxide was needed for oxidation to occur.

Armed with this information, Meyerhof first activated a muscle without oxygen, and studied it. He discovered that a certain amount of lactic acid collected in the muscle in exact proportion to the amount of work being done by the muscle. At the same time, a similar amount of glycogen disappeared. Then Meyerhof activated a muscle with oxygen. When the muscle received oxygen, the lactic acid disappeared and the muscle required additional oxygen. Again, the amount of lactic acid which disappeared was in direct proportion to the additional oxygen required. The oxygen was only enough for oxidation of a small part of the lactic acid that disappeared. The remainder, some 70 to 80 percent of the lactic acid, turned to glycogen.

Dr. Meyerhof (left) at the dinner for Nobel Prize recipients

In 1924, Meyerhof was appointed department head of the Kaiser Wilhelm Institute near Berlin; in 1929, he was made director of the Physiology Department. Nine years later, he left Germany and lived in Paris for two years. Then he went to America, at the invitation of the University of Pennsylvania, where he worked until his death.

Otto Meyerhof was not only a brilliant researcher, he was also a clear thinking observer of the political scene. In a speech in 1949, he presented a profound analysis of the German situation, pointing out that moral and ethical law had been trampled out of existence. Quoting the German philosopher Immanuel Kant, he noted bitterly: "If justice is refused, there is no reason for human life on earth."

ALBERT ABRAHAM
MICHELSON
1852-1931

In 1877, a 25-year-old naval officer, Albert Michelson, sent light through a half mile of tubing, bounced it off mirrors and became the first man in history to measure the speed of light.

Years later Albert Einstein, speaking at a scientific convention, said, "You, Dr. Michelson, drew physicists to new paths, and with your wonderful experiments you paved the way for the theory of relativity."

For his work with light, Michelson became the first American ever to win a Nobel Prize.

When Michelson made his measurement, other scientists were already probing for the same information. The well-known astronomer Simon Newcomb had been given a grant by the United States government to find the answer. Before then, scientist James Clark Maxwell had a theory that light traveled faster in air than in water. There were others who thought that light always traveled at the same speed. Maxwell theorized that the speed of light should be about 186,300 miles per second. Michelson's first measurement was about this speed.

The result of Michelson's first experiments were published in the *American Journal of Science* in May 1878. In the summer, the young scientist was given an allowance of two hundred dollars to perfect his device. In 1879, the *New York Times* wrote, "A brilliant new name has been added to American science." In this same year, Michelson told a gathering of distinguished scientists that his measurement of the speed of light was 185,508 miles per second. Simon Newcomb, also trying to solve the problem, accepted the findings.

The method Michelson used was, of course, more important than the corrections which he himself later made. Maxwell had arrived at almost the correct answer theoretically. Measuring light by actual experiment with physical proof was Michelson's unique contribution. No scientist questioned the measurements, but Michelson himself. Forty-five years later, in 1927, he published his final correction.

Michelson worked on other important problems relating to

Dr. Michelson measuring light

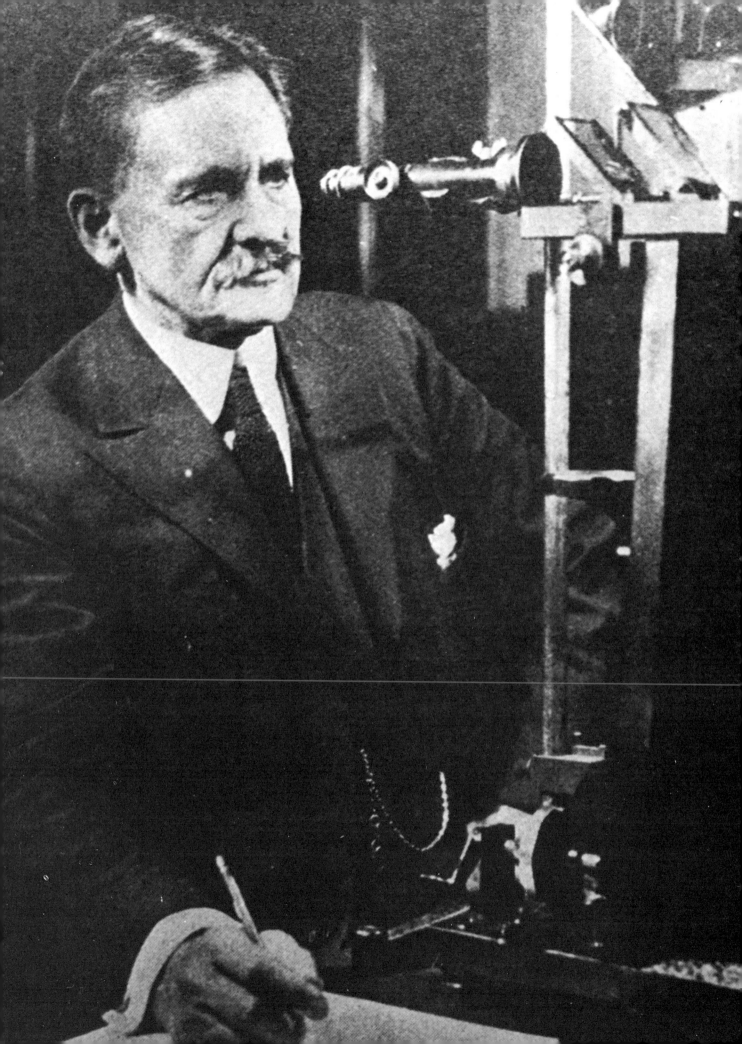

light. In 1881, he left the Navy to become Professor of Physics at Cleveland. There he began to look into how light moves. Physicists had long believed that space was filled with something called "ether" and that light "rode" on it. Michelson questioned whether there really was such a thing as ether. Working with Professor Edward Morley, Michelson sought to calculate the speed of light in relation to ether. They tried experiments in day and night and in different seasons. They were hoping that at least one measurement would show that the earth moved at a higher speed, compared to the ether, but found no difference. Since Michelson could neither measure nor find ether, Albert Einstein and others came to the conclusion that there was no ether.

This discovery led Einstein to his theory of relativity and paved the way for modern physics. Michelson had shown that the speed of light never changes. Einstein insisted that new formulas would have to be developed based on the assumption that the only permanent thing on the earth is the speed of light — it never changes, but everything else in the world, even time and motion, is relative.

BORIS PASTERNAK
1890-1960

Although Boris Pasternak is famous today as the author of one of the masterpieces of modern literature, *Dr. Zhivago,* his first love was music. He studied musical composition under the composer Scriabin, whom he knew well. Pasternak's mother was a

During a visit to New York, Pasternak gestures as he talks to Mr. and Mrs. Leonard Bernstein, David Keiser, President of the New York Philharmonic and impresario Sol Hurok

Battle scene from the movie "Dr. Zhivago"

musican, his father a painter. The young Boris also studied law at Moscow University and philosophy at the University of Marburg in Germany.

The outbreak of World War I brought him home to Russia, where he worked in a factory in the Urals. There, and later in Moscow, he lived through the terror and excitement of the Russian Revolution of 1917.

He later became renowned as a poet, as the best Russian translator of Shakespeare and Goethe, and also as the writer of beautiful lyrics. His knowledge and broad experience, combined with superb command of the Russian language, gave him a special place in Soviet literature. When, ten years or so after the Revolution, the new regime demanded strict obedience from Soviet writers, insisting that their works deal only with approved subjects in the "correct" style of socialist-realism, severe criticism was leveled at Pasternak by the extremists. However, in 1932 he was fully rehabilitated and at the Congress of Soviet Writers in 1934 was acclaimed the most important Soviet poet of his generation.

Pasternak completed *Dr. Zhivago* in 1955, after working on it for ten years. During the "thaw" following the Stalinist regime, intellectuals in the Soviet Union were freer of party control and Pasternak sent his manuscript to an Italian communist publisher in Milan, Feltrinelli Editore. An agreement was signed for the publication of the epic novel in both Russian and Italian. The Soviet Writers' Association vetoed its publication, claiming that the novel described the Russian Revolution "...as if it were one of the sins in Russian history," and demanded a correction. Their apprehension was partly based on the fact that the novel took a detached and sometimes critical view of communism, resulting in such observations as: "I do not know of any flow of thought which is more isolated and more removed from the facts than Marxism."

Pasternak accepted the verdict and asked Feltrinelli to return the manuscript. The publisher rejected the request, claiming that the writer was acting under pressure. The Russians found the matter so important that they sent Alexei Surkov, the secretary of the Soviet Writers' Association, to Milan. Feltrinelli was unimpressed and continued his preparations for publishing the book, claim-

The Russian "dacha" where Pasternak lived and died

ing that he was thereby doing "a service to the author." When the Nobel Prize for Literature was awarded to Pasternak in 1958, it appeared that Feltrinelli had been right. Under pressure from the Soviet authorities, who refused him permission to go to Oslo to receive the Prize, Pasternak refused to accept it.

Pasternak's work teaches very simply that even after a revolution like the one in 1917, after so much sorrow and inhumanity in the name of progress and humanity, people retain a sense of

129

truth, love of life and hope survive, and the power of the word is valued just as it was in the days of Pushkin.

Pasternak himself set great store by his novel. In reply to the editor of a Uruguayan pamphlet, who had expressed appreciation of his poetic works, Pasternak said: "Those were trivial. I feel that we are witness to the birth of an entirely new era that will continue to grow even without our knowledge ....It is being formed in silence and has never been officially recognized ...I think that the best of my works to this day is the novel, *Dr. Zhivago*. Because of saddening circumstances, I had one-sided publicity."

Pasternak did not change his mind about man's quest for truth and for freedom. A poem written by him shortly before his death, which reached the English newspaper *The Daily Mail* proves this. In it he says:

"I was lost like an animal in its cage,
Somewhere there is freedom and light,
Behind me rises the tumult of persecution and there
is nowhere to flee.
Let it be when it will be, I, upon the brink of my
grave, stand,
Believing that the time will come and good will overcome evil."

WOLFGANG PAULI
1900-1958

It was in 1945 that two atomic bombs were dropped for the first time. That same year, the Nobel Prize for Physics was given to an Austrian Jewish scientist, Wolfgang Pauli, for his work in atomic physics.

Pauli was only twenty-five years old when he formulated a principle crucial to the development of atomic power: the Pauli Exclusion Principle. Essentially, this sets forth that within every atom the electrons move on their own predetermined circuits and are "forbidden" or excluded from moving on the same track as another atom.

Pauli's father, also a famous scientist, was professor of biochemistry at the University of Vienna. He soon recognized his son's talent and sent him to Munich to study under Professor Sommerfeld, a leading researcher in the field of theoretical physics. Professor Sommerfeld quickly perceived the young man's extraordinary intelligence and made him his permanent assistant. Pauli later went on to become assistant to Niels Bohr, the most important atomic scientist of his time.

Pauli wrote his doctorate on Einstein's theory of relativity. His professors said it was the best and most profound explanation they had ever read on the subject. By the age of twenty-six, Pauli had become a professor at Hamburg University. Einstein himself was so impressed with Pauli's work that in 1939 he invited him to Princeton University and there they worked together at the Institute for Advanced Study.

Pauli published several important research papers on heat of metals and their electrical charge, the "Beta disintegration" phenomenon and the "neutrino" particle, thereby opening new horizons in thermodynamics and atomic research.

Just eighteen months before his sudden death, Pauli took part in the Atomic Conference at the Weizmann Institute in Rehovot.

Towards the end of his life, Pauli, under the influence of the Jung school of psychology, crystallized the view that the foundations of scientific research do not lie in logic alone. Spiritual

Prof. Pauli arrives in Stockholm with his wife to attend 1946 Nobel presentation ceremonies

factors — natural intuition, imagination and the subconscious — play a part. He became convinced that religious consciousness also has an important role in the formation of the spirit and the motivation of the researcher. He studied many mystic movements and was particularly interested in the cabala. During his visit to Israel he visited the synagogues in Safed and the orthodox quarter of Mea Shearim in Jerusalem and studied the books on cabala of Professor Gershom Scholem. He wrote to a friend, "I saw the sunrise in Jerusalem and the sunset on the Acropolis. Two worlds were connected in my eyes, the Jewish and the Greek, which have given to the world the foundations of culture."

Pauli, a man of the highest ethical ideals, was deeply shocked by atomic experiments and by the threats of nuclear warfare. The use of the atom bomb caused a severe spiritual crisis within him and undermined his belief in the ethical basis of science. "I do not know the right way," he said, "but it is clear to me that we must look for the connection between science and ethics and humanism."

At his funeral, two scientists eulogized Pauli, but the most significant remark was a brief statement made by the American Jewish scientist, Professor Rabi, who said, "Pauli was the conscience of physics."

ISIDOR RABI
1898-

In this age of nuclear weapons which could lead to world annihilation, it is not enough that a scientist serve as a technological adviser; today no scientist can avoid the responsibility and ultimate consequences of his discoveries. He must also strive for recognition so that his opinion carries weight. This summarizes the view of Professor Isidor Rabi, who succeeded in measuring the atom with a precision never before attained.

Isidor Rabi received a great stimulus to his scientific research during an extensive visit to Europe from 1927 to 1930. He spent most of his time at the Hamburg laboratory of Professor Otto Stern, where he watched the great Jewish scholar measuring the magnetic moments of the atom. Upon his return to America, Rabi continued his atomic research. He succeeded in measuring the properties of the atom with an exactness one hundred times greater than could be obtained previously. When awarding the Nobel Prize to Rabi in 1944, the president of the Physics Section of the Nobel Prize Committee said, "Many have held the theory of a relationship between the minutest particles of matter, electrons, and the nucleus of an atom... Rabi's experiments clearly prove that there exists in the atom a magnetic force which will react when it is placed between two ends of a magnet."

Rabi was among the eminent atomic scientists who demanded, in an open letter to *The New York Times* on February 16, 1946, that the President of the United States order immediate cessation of work on the hydrogen bomb. Rabi urged that the distilled plutonium and uranium 235 used in atomic research be deposited in the depths of the sea or returned to their original form. However, when it was learned that Russia had developed her own atomic weapon and had in some aspects progressed even further than the United States, American scientists proceeded in the production of the hydrogen bomb.

Rabi and eight other scientists were appointed to the Committee for Consultation on Atomic Energy Affairs, with Robert Oppenheimer at its head. The committee accepted Oppenheimer's stand

Dr. Rabi receives the Niels Bohr Gold Medal from King Frederik of Denmark

opposing further production of the hydrogen bomb based on the conviction that the hydrogen bomb possessed such incalculable destructive power that no civilized people had the right to assist in its production. The decision was passed by a majority. Only two members, Rabi and Enrico Fermi, voiced a minority opinion. They

Dr. Rabi being congratulated by Norway's Princess Martha, after receiving the Nobel Prize

Dr. Rabi (center) poses with the nuclear scientists Dr. W. Bennett Lewis of Canada (left) and Dr. Betrand L. Goldschmidt of Paris, after the three received the 1967 Atoms for Peace Award

suggested that the United States first attempt to meet Russia halfway with a system of control and inspection of all types of atomic weapons; if they failed to reach such an agreement, production would be justified. However, Rabi agreed with Oppenheimer and others that a strong air defense could guarantee the security of the United States even without the hydrogen bomb.

Rabi has received many awards and honorary degrees for his work. He was appointed United States delegate to the Scientific

Committee of the International Agency of Atomic Energy, served on the Scientific Committees of NATO and the United Nations, the Scientific Committee of the Disarmament Agency and on the Scientific Committee advising the President of the United States. In 1957 he served as Chairman of the Advisory Committee of the U.S. Atomic Energy Commission, but retired following a heart attack.

Acutely aware of the awesome implications involved in the creation of atomic weapons, Rabi has tried to combine his scientific achievements with a humanist's moral concern for the future of mankind.

TADEUSZ REICHSTEIN
1897-

To most people with acute arthritis, the name Tadeusz Reichstein is unknown. But his work on the adrenal cortex has transformed arthritis from a dread disease which left its victims confined to wheelchairs and sick with pain, to one which may be almost completely controlled.

Professor Reichstein was awarded the Nobel Prize for medicine and physiology in 1950, sharing it with two American scientists, Dr. Edward Calvin Kendall, a professor of physiological chemistry, and Dr. Philip Showalter Hench, a specialist in rheumatic diseases, both of Rochester, Minnesota. The three men were honored "for their discoveries concerning the suprarenal cortex hormones, their structure and biological effects."

Professor Reichstein's work on the amazing chemical factory, the adrenal cortex, took place in the Technical College in Zurich and later at the University of Basle, where he was head of the Pharmacological Institute. The Reichstein family came to Switzerland by way of Wloclawek, Poland; Kiev, in the Ukraine; and Berlin, where they moved in 1905, following the Kishinev pogrom. They became Swiss citizens in 1914, when young Tadeusz left his private tutors and began regular schooling. Two years later, he enrolled at the Zurich Technical College, and was graduated as a chemical engineer in 1920.

Deciding that he preferred an academic to an industrial career, the young man returned to the Technical College and received a doctorate in 1922. He was named assistant to a well-known organic chemist, Herman Staudinger. When Staudinger moved to the University of Freiburg in 1925, Reichstein became the assistant of Staudinger's successor, the Yugoslav chemist Leopold Ruzicka, winner of the Nobel Prize in 1939. Reichstein later added teaching to his research work, and in 1932 achieved his first great laboratory success, the synthesis of vitamin C. This was followed by his investigations into the hormones manufactured by the adrenal cortex and he gave the name "adrenosterone" to the first of 28 cortical hormones which he isolated. It was in 1937 that he isolated the sub-

Dr. Reichstein (center) being honored at 1950 Nobel presentation ceremony

stance "corticosterone," later identified as substance E among the six compounds isolated independently by Dr. Kendall in Minnesota. It was this substance which proved to have such a therapeutic effect on arthritis.

NELLY SACHS
1891-

"We arrived in Stockholm physically and spiritually crushed. Mother relived the torments of oppression each night anew — poverty, illness, utter despair. I still do not know how we endured it all. But faith and love in mankind gave me courage. It was at this time that I wrote *Dwelling Places of Death,* followed shortly by *Eli.*" So wrote Nelly Sachs, the German-Jewish poetess who was saved from the Nazi inferno in 1940 through the intervention of Swedish writer Selma Lagerlof and members of the Swedish royal family.

Before the Nazis came to power, her writings dealt with the human condition of mankind in general; from the day of her rescue, she devoted herself exclusively to the bitter fate of her people and to the misery and despair of persecuted people everywhere, and in all times.

Once asked whether she considered herself a Jewish, Swedish or German writer, Nelly Sachs had answered, "And why is that important? I see myself as a person." Although she remained unmoved by Jewish national strivings, her poems are distinctly Jewish in subject matter.

Her works fall into three main categories: drama, translations from Swedish into German, and poetry. Written in rich yet simple language, her poetry is replete with associations from the terrible years under the Nazi regime. In *Sufferings of Israel,* she describes the terrors of World War II in symbolic images. There is no evading the meaning of the *Dwelling Places of Death.* The first poem in the series describes the body of the nation rising in smoke through a chimney. In other poems, she tells of the children left motherless, of the thin line between life and death, and of tattoos bearing the stamp of death. An often repeated motif in her poetry is a reference to a pile of orphaned shoes which remain without owners — their owners were Jewish children sent to the gas chambers.

On October 18, 1965, Nelly Sachs was awarded the German Book Publishers' Peace Prize at a ceremony in Frankfurt. The citation accompanying the prize of 10,000 marks stated: "The lyrical

Nelly Sachs receives the Nobel Prize from the King of Sweden

works of Nelly Sachs are devoted to the fate of the Jew in an era when humaneness and amity take precedence over national and religious divisions." The German publishers had singled out a woman author for the first time, and indicated that two reasons for her selection were that she had remained faithful to the German language, and was able to respond to persecution with "forgiving love." In 1966 she was awarded the Nobel Prize in Literature.

EMILIO GINO SEGRE
1905-

Among the many discoveries of the past three decades that have revolutionized man's conception of the structure of the universe, none was more revolutionary than that made in 1955 by Emilio Segre and Owen Chamberlain, two physicists at the University of California in Berkeley. This team, experimenting with a specially-built 184-inch synchro-cyclotron, discovered within the atom's nucleus a new particle, negatively charged but of the same mass as the proton.

This discovery — which brought the pair the Nobel Prize in 1959 — was viewed by many scientists as the most important of the decade. Since the early 1930's, much of the scientific world believed that with the knowledge of the structure of the atom, matter had been reduced to its ultimate. Atoms, it was held, consist of three types of particles : positively-charged protons, negatively-charged electrons, and uncharged neutrons. The protons and neutrons are contained in the nucleus of the atom, which has a positive charge. Around the nucleus in various configurations are electrons equal in number to the protons in the nucleus ; thus the atom as a whole would be normally neutral.

This theory however did not explain a number of phenomena, and was challenged by some scientists, among them the British physicist F.A.M. Derek. In 1931, Derek published a mathematical equation demonstrating in an exact and quantitative way the various characteristics of the electron. His equation led to the conclusion that within the atom there existed a particle similar to the electron in every way except that it had a positive charge. Soon Derek's theory was verified. Karl B. Anderson of the University of California, during research in cosmic radiation, discovered positive electrons among the particles produced by this radiation. These particles were named positrons.

The discovery of the positron challenged physicists to search for other fundamental particles whose existence was indicated by Derek's theory. If there exists a "reverse" electron, there must also be a "reverse" proton — a fundamental particle whose weight and

Dr. Segre (second from left) with fellow Nobel Prize winners

other characteristics resembled those of the proton but bearing an electrically negative charge instead of a positive charge. But to produce such a particle artificially, tremendous energy would be needed: it would be necessary to bombard fundamental particles like protons in the hope that the collisions would cause the formation of the antiproton. For this purpose, a special apparatus, the gigantic cyclotron called "Bevatron" was built by Segre, Chamberlain and their colleagues at the University of California at Berkeley.

Their experiments were eventually successful. They isolated a

Dr. Segre (center) with two of his associates at the University of California Lawrence Radiation Laboratory: Clyde Wiegand (left) and Herbert M. Steiner

Dr. Segre with his family at their home in Lafayette, California

particle that exactly resembled the proton except that it bore a negative charge. In October 1955, when the scientists succeeded in isolating 60 antiprotons, they briefly mentioned their discovery in a scientific paper. Their announcement caused great excitement, for it opened the way to the existence of a "reverse world" constructed of "reverse material" which may be unable to coexist with regular material. As the New York Times noted in 1955, the giant cyclotron was "a powerful new tool for probing the mysterious realms of the nuclei of atoms and the forces that hold the universe together."

The discovery of the antiproton climaxed decades of study and research by Emilio Segre. He was born in Tivoli, Italy, and studied engineering and physics at the University of Rome. A student of the renowned Enrico Fermi, one of the fathers of atomic science, he later worked with Fermi and participated in the discovery of neutrons. He became an instructor and assistant professor of physics at his *alma mater,* and from 1936 to 1938 taught at the University of Palermo.

A Jew, Segre foresaw the dire results that were to follow the anti-Semitism then rife in his country, and in 1938 emigrated to the United States. At Berkeley, he worked with Dr. Glenn T. Seaborg, one of the pioneers in atomic investigation, participating in the discovery in 1940 of Uranium 239, and of plutonium.

As an expert in the field of nuclear fission, Segre was invited in 1943 to join the large group of scientists who produced the first atomic bomb in Los Alamos. After the war, Segre returned to Berkeley to continue his research and eventually discover the antiproton.

OTTO STERN
1888-

The studies of Otto Stern unlocked one of the great mysteries faced by modern scientists: what is the force that holds together the protons within the infinitesimally small nucleus of the atom? Professor Stern postulated that the proton is like a tiny magnet, and possesses a magnetic moment which holds the protons together like "cosmic cement." The force of the magnetic moment of the proton is millions of times greater than the electrical repelling forces, which threaten to tear the atom asunder and thus reduce the material universe to a cloud of hydrogen.

With another scientist, Walter Gerlach, Stern developed a method of measuring the magnetic moments of atoms and later refined this method to measure those of atomic nuclei. His experiments proved the validity of the all-important Quantum Mechanics Theory. For his discovery, Stern was awarded the 1943 Nobel Prize in Physics.

Otto Stern was born in Sorau, Germany, in 1888. He studied physics and chemistry at Breslau University, and earned his doctorate in 1912. The brilliant young physicist then worked with Albert Einstein, first in Prague and then in Zurich. In 1921, he was appointed associate professor of theoretical physics at the University of Rostock, and was promoted two years later to professor of physical chemistry and director of the laboratory at the University of Hamburg.

Along with so many other renowned Jewish scientists, Stern fled Germany during the Nazi rise to power, and came to settle in the United States. He was named research professor in physics at the Carnegie Institute of Technology in 1933.

Dr. Stern (second from left) with fellow Nobel Prize winners

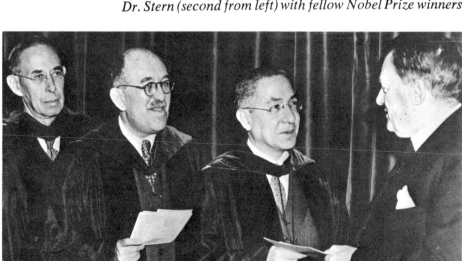

SELMAN ABRAHAM WAKSMAN
1888-

Philadelphia — January, 1945: Sixty people are suddenly stricken with typhus. The symptoms are high fever, loss of consciousness and internal bleeding, ominous signs of approaching death. Neither penicillin nor sulfadine, two new "miracle drugs," are effective in stopping the rapid deterioration of the patients' condition. Therefore, in desperation, one of the most critically ill is selected to receive an experimental injection of a newly developed but as yet unproven drug. Within 18 hours reduced fever, regained consciousness and cessation of bleeding signal the end of an epidemic. The power of streptomycin, an antibiotic developed only a few months earlier by Dr. Waksman, has been dramatically demonstrated.

The discovery of penicillin in 1942 spurred a search by bacteriologists all over the world for other antibiotics capable of combatting diseases unaffected by penicillin, such as tuberculosis, cholera, dysentery, typhus and leprosy. Nearly 85 types of bacterial molds were developed between 1942 and 1944, but all were either ineffective or toxic. It was not until Dr. Waksman, a well-known earth-bacteriologist, developed streptomycin that the breakthrough was made.

Dr. Waksman found streptomycin by studying thousands of compounds. Of these, only one thousand succeeded in destroying primitive types of bacteria; only one hundred gave promise of good results in further research; and only ten were chosen for final intensive study.

At the end of 1943, Dr. Waksman and his young assistant, Dr. Albert Satel, had isolated the *streptomyces griseus,* a strong strain of bacteria which attacked and annihilated any disease bacteria fed to it, including typhus. The next phase was to extract the toxic chemical, which they had named "streptomycin." Waksman did not have the necessary equipment in his laboratories at Rutgers University for developing the new medicine and consequently he moved to the larger laboratories of Merck, Inc. in New York.

The remaining problem was to determine whether the human

system could tolerate the poison. When a preliminary test performed on rats indicated the possibility that streptomycin could be administered to humans without harmful effects, the laboratory directors put 50 researchers at Waksman's disposal. Soon it became evident

Dr. Waksman (right) in his laboratory (1952)

that the properties of streptomycin were more valuable than even its developer had anticipated, and that large doses did not have the destructive qualities of drugs such as sulfa.

Dr. Selman Abraham Waksman won the Nobel Prize in 1952 for discovering one of the most versatile and effective drugs ever known. One of streptomycin's most dramatic uses has been against deadly tuberculosis. The drug has saved more lives than were lost in all of Napoleon's wars.

OTTO WALLACH
1847-1931

For many years, scientists had tried to perfect a method which would enable them to determine the chemical makeup of various compounds. They succeeded only in analyzing the most simple substances found in nature. Otto Wallach, a German scientist, devoted his life to this problem, and so important were his discoveries that he was awarded the Nobel Prize in 1910 for his achievements in organic and industrial chemistry, as well as for his pioneer work in the field of alicyclic compounds.

The properties of chemical compounds do not depend on their composition only; rather, their makeup is determined to a large degree by their atomic arrangement in a molecule. The molecule is similar to a room containing various furniture pieces which can be arranged in different ways. The composition of the room will always be the same, but its appearance will change every time the furniture is rearranged. Therefore, if we want to understand the chemical essence of drugs, and various materials, we must find out not only the basic compounds which are contained in them but also their molecular arrangement.

The earliest organic chemists devoted themselves to the study of the properties of compounds, but little progress was made until Adolf von Bayer (1835-1917), a famous German scientist, discovered compounds that are present in certain strong-smelling vegetables. Because of their high volatility, they were called "ethereal oils." They contain a special kind of carbohydrate found in resin. Not only liquid resin can be made from these oils, but also solids such as pitch.

Wallach, while lecturing on ethereal oils, became interested in their composition, especially as his teacher and associate, Professor Friedrich August Kekule von Stradonitz, stated in his presence that no chemist would ever be able to separate the substances in these oils. He began his research by systematically investigating all the oils used in pharmaceutics. These were usually produced by distillation of organic matter. By further distillation, Wallach managed to separate the substances, and to identify them. Most of the substances were alike in their basic chemical makeup; each molecule had six carbon atoms combined with a greater number of hydrogen atoms.

By 1884 Wallach had begun his study of resin and pitch, and within the first six years of his research he was able to identify ten new substances and to distinguish between them. He was the first scientist to study resin matter and to point out the similarities between numerous chemical compounds. This had important implications not only for pure science but also for industrial chemistry dealing with ethereal oil products.

Until Wallach's time, every manufacturer did what he liked in industrial chemistry. The market was flooded with adulterated, valueless products which no one could test or prove harmful. Once Wallach had studied and publicized the contents of each and every known pharmaceutical compound, such practices were put to a

stop. Moreover, he designed reliable analytic methods for discovering imperfect products, not only by chemical means but also by optical and physical methods. His work had a great influence on the perfume industry. He also worked on the transformation of chloral into dichloric acid. He synthesized chlorides and investigated azotic and diazotic compounds.

Otto Wallach was born in 1847 in Königsberg, the capital of Eastern Prussia. He studied chemistry at the Universities of Göttingen and Berlin, and received a doctorate in philosophy in 1869 from the University of Göttingen. He taught and did research in Berlin and then was invited to work with Professor Kekule in Bonn. Wallach had a lifelong interest in art and the nearness of Bonn to the rich art treasures of Belgium and Holland was one of the reasons he readily moved there. Later, he worked for the huge Agfa company which manufactured anilin outside Berlin. But pure research interested Wallach more than industry and he returned to Bonn in 1876, where he resumed his research work and also taught as a professor. In 1889 he went back to Göttingen where he worked for 25 years until he retired in 1915. From then until his death, he devoted himself entirely to art.

OTTO HEINRICH WARBURG
1883-

Otto Heinrich Warburg was born in Germany of a family prominent in the world of science and in Jewish affairs. Another Warburg, also named Otto, was the Chairman of the World Zionist Congress at one time and contributed greatly toward the creation of the state of Israel. Felix Warburg, of the American branch of the family, was one of the leaders of American Jewry and instrumental in setting up the Joint Distribution Committee and the United Jewish Appeal. There have been Warburgs in several branches of science, including botany and physics.

In 1906, Otto Warburg completed his college studies, after which he studied medicine. His early and abiding interest was in the physiology of cells, particularly how they breathe.

In 1911 he wrote his Ph.D. dissertation on cell respiration based on experiments he had carried out in Naples and Heidelberg. He was soon appointed director of the cell physiology department of the Kaiser Wilhelm Institute in Berlin, and being independent financially, was able to devote himself exclusively to research. He became very attached to the Institute, which was the largest and best-endowed in Germany. He served in the German army during World War I and came back after the war to continue his work.

In 1931 Warburg received the Nobel Prize in physiology and medicine for his discovery of the nature and mode of action of the respiratory enzyme known as Warburg's yellow enzyme.

Warburg has also made important contributions to the understanding of cancer. Thousands of researchers are trying to find a solution to this dread disease wherein the body cells undergo a pathological change, growing wildly, extending into surrounding tissues, and spreading to other parts of the body. This leads to death if the disease is not caught in time. Warburg's theory holds that cancer is caused by the faulty breathing of cells and not by a foreign agent. When a man stops absorbing enough oxygen, the cell's breathing is weakened and this situation becomes chronic. Cancer cells, he found, need less oxygen than the healthy cells, and so cells which do not receive oxygen discard the normal rules

Prof. Warburg and assistant Oswald Tippo at the University of Illinois laboratory

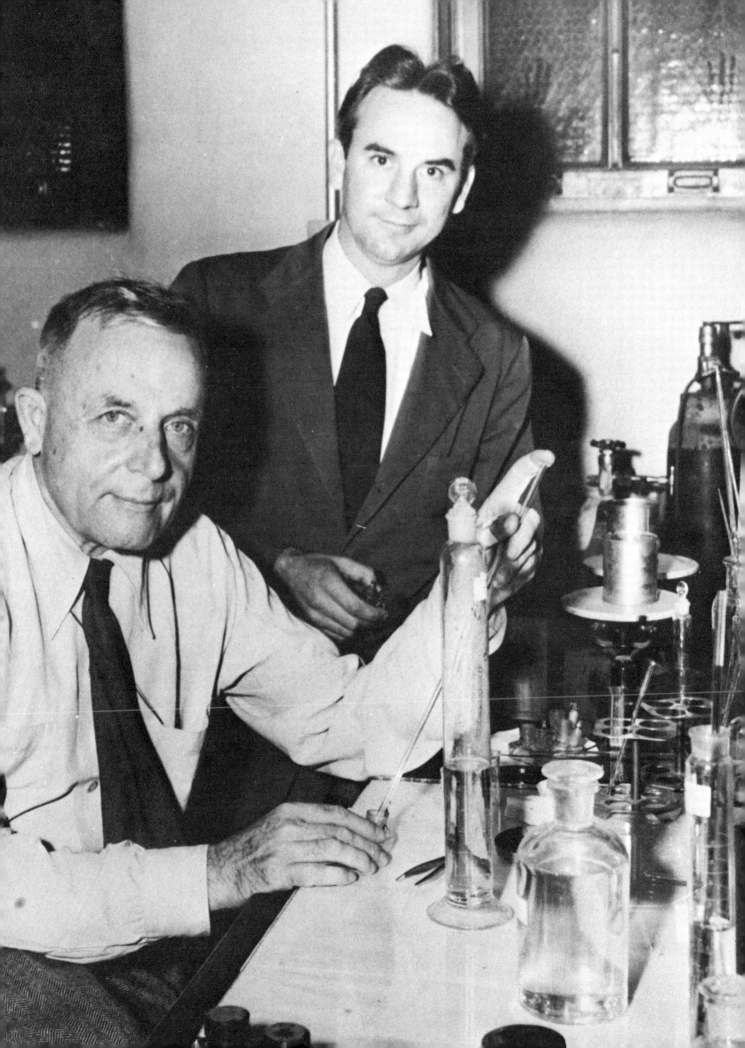

under which the body functions and begin to form malignant growths.

Based on this theory, his advice for the prevention of cancer is to stay away from chemically-produced fumes, avoid aniline dyes in food, and to reduce cigarette smoking — in short, to avoid anything that limits the supply of oxygen to the body.

In addition to his investigation of the metabolism of tumors and the respiration of cells, Warburg made an abiding contribution to the study of the exchange of energy in the assimilation of carbonic acid in plants. Warburg was interested in the chemical reactions and the working of light in photosynthesis. The energy needed for making one molecule of oxygen and carbohydrate was measured. He found that the energy needed did not come only from the sun's rays, but also from the plant itself, by a previously unknown biological process. With this breakthrough the understanding of photosynthesis has been made much clearer.

EUGENE PAUL WIGNER
1902-

In 1938, a meeting took place which may have changed the history of the world. Refugee Jewish physicists who had escaped or been driven from Europe by the Nazis, gathered together in the United States. They were worried that the United States seemed to be losing the race to smash the atom. The German Government had been aiding its scientists, but the American Government was doing very little to develop an atomic weapon. These physicists knew that Germany was first in atomic research and that the free countries of the world were asleep.

One of the world's most important figures in theoretical and applied physics, Eugene Paul Wigner, recounted: "When two German scientists made an important discovery in 1939, a friend and I realized that the new discovery might eventually become a basis for a monstrous military weapon." Together with Leo Szilard, a Jewish-Hungarian physicist, Wigner asked Professor Albert Einstein to write to President Roosevelt. Einstein was the only person with enough prestige to prod the President into action at once. Government decisions usually took years, but now there was no time — delay would be fatal.

Einstein wrote his famous warning about German physicists and the atomic bomb on August 2, 1939, just one month before World War II began. On October 11, Roosevelt gave instructions for atomic energy to be studied and an atomic bomb to be developed in the United States if possible. Thus was born the "Manhattan Project."

For 40 years Wigner has been at the center of all the scientific developments in atomic research. In 1926 he was only a departmental assistant in physics at the Technion in Berlin. A year later, he was already doing important work at one of the key centers for atomic research in Germany. He seems to have anticipated the rise of the Nazis, as he left Germany two years before they came to power. He went to Princeton University to work on various research projects.

Wigner did not believe in secrecy in science. He told the U.S.

Senate that trying to keep the atom bomb and its development a secret would only slow down research in America. He felt that other countries would catch up within a year. Although his efforts in America were devoted to the development of the bomb, he was worried about using it, because of the terrible destruction it could cause. "This weapon should not be used except after adequate warning," he wrote.

Wigner organized a World Atomic Physicists Meeting in 1946,

A Swedish diplomatic attendant (right) explains the Nobel Diploma to the Wigner family (1963)

in which 100 great physicists took part. In the same year, he received the Medal of Merit of the National Academy of Sciences, and supervised the work of 400 scientists at Oak Ridge. In 1950, he received the Franklin Medal for his work in atomic physics, in 1958 the Enrico Fermi Prize and in 1960 the Atoms for Peace Prize.

In 1963, Wigner received the highest award known in the world of science, the Nobel Prize for Physics. There has been one major disappointment in his life. His hope that the discovery of the atomic and hydrogen bombs would lead to a strong United Nations to control them, and bring about peace, has as yet been unfulfilled.

Dr. Wigner (left) holds a bound citation which accompanies a solid gold medal, as he accepts a check for $50,000 from the Atomic Energy Commission Chairman John McCone. . .all part of the AEC's Enrico Fermi Award which he received in 1958

RICHARD WILLSTÄTTER
1872-1942

RICHARD WILLSTÄTTER

The young scientist usually went swimming every morning in a pool in the suburbs of Munich. One day, noticing the drops of dew glistening on leaves and flower petals, he wondered why nature favored the color green, and what the true nature of this green was, which botanists called chlorophyll. Many chemists had tried to discover its secret and all their efforts had yielded no results. Richard Willstätter finally penetrated the mysteries of the wonder-substance, chlorophyll. It was he who first explained the biochemistry of plants.

In 1913, Willstätter released his first findings on chlorophyll, and two years later was awarded the Nobel Prize in Chemistry for his revolutionary studies and the conclusions reached through them. The sun, he found, is the source of all living energy. When its rays hit a green leaf, an extraordinary process takes place: the chlorophyll synthesizes carbohydrates from carbon dioxide and water, forming free oxygen as a byproduct. Thus, each plant leaf can be seen as a source of life as well as a small chemical factory.

Willstätter next asked how man could make use of green plants for medicinal purposes. He found that simple chlorophyll took on a completely new form when it came in contact with living cells in a human being, exerting great strength against microbes. What was the reason for this change? He finally determined that microbes live only in wounds cut off from air. When chlorophyll is injected into the wounded area, a chemical process is set into motion which transforms the carbon dioxide concentrated in the body to oxygen. The bacteria cannot combat the effects of the oxygen, and cannot reproduce. Thus the body is able to again resume normal functions.

In 1912, Willstätter took over the directorship of the Kaiser Wilhelm Institute in Berlin. With the outbreak of World War I, he was given the task of developing a filter for gas masks. The Germans had introduced gas warfare and feared that their enemies would also use it. Willstätter produced the filter, and Germany was able to manufacture thirty million gas masks by 1917. He also worked

Dr. Wilstätter in his laboratory

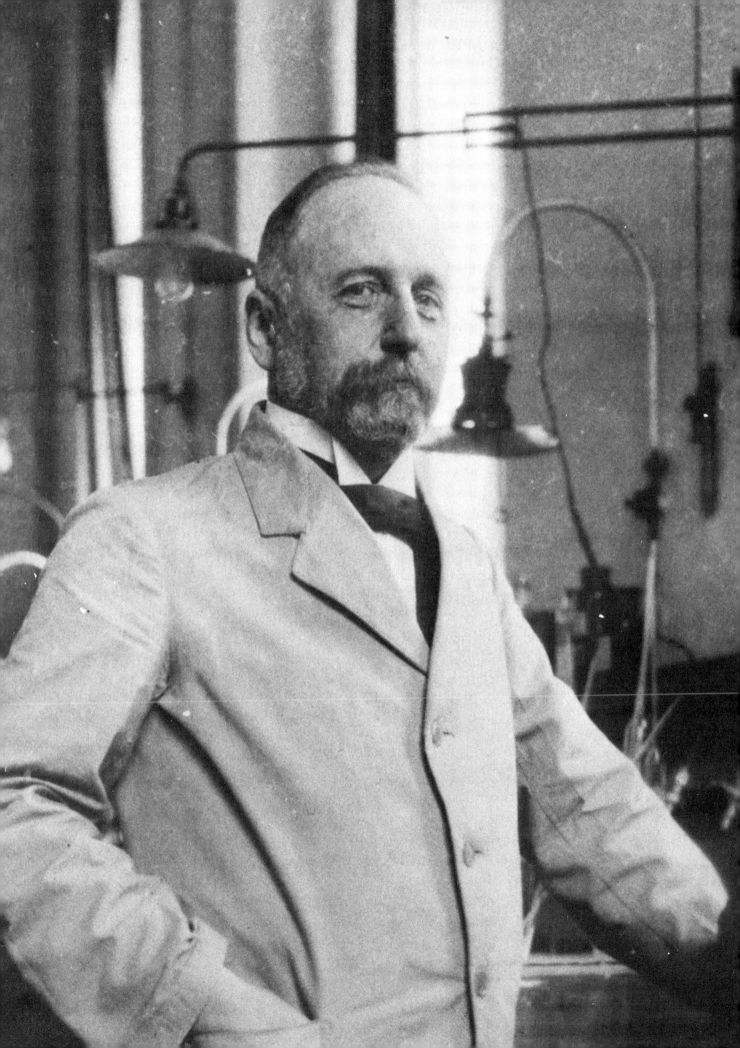

on new principles of inducing sleep and developed a new type of sleeping pill.

Willstätter was invited to return to Munich as a professor, but that city was rapidly becoming a hotbed of anti-Semitism. As a matter of fact, after King Ludwig III of Bavaria signed the document appointing Willstätter a professor, he threw down his pen and shouted to his education minister: "This is the last time I will approve the appointment of a Jew!" In 1925 Willstätter learned that a certain Professor Goldschmidt had been denied an important position because he was Jewish, and he immediately handed in his resignation. Although the Kaiser Wilhelm Institute in Berlin invited him to return, he refused the honor and also turned down invitations from other universities. He was not, however, permitted to leave Germany.

His achievements and the worldwide respect he commanded did not help him when the Nazis rose to power. On the night of November 9, 1938, Gestapo agents came to take him to a concentration camp, but they did not find him. The old man was in his garden, taking care of his roses; the plants to which he had devoted his life had saved him. The Nazis however, confiscated everything he owned, including his vast scientific library. International protests protected him from bodily harm, yet the government still refused to allow him to leave the country. When he tried to cross the border into Switzerland, he was apprehended and returned to Munich. Again world protest intervened, and Willstätter was finally given a passport to Switzerland, where he settled and wrote his memoirs. Toward the end of the book we find a passage typical of his outlook about the political events of his time: "When Aristides the Just, who was later expelled from his homeland, was asked what hurt him most in exile, he answered: 'The fact that my homeland could fall so low as to expel me.'"

INDEX